# PSYCHOTROPIC DRUGS IN THE YEAR 2000

## THE YEAR 2000

### Use By Normal Humans

# PSYCHOTROPIC DRUGS IN THE YEAR 2000

## Use By Normal Humans

*Compiled and Edited by*

**WAYNE O. EVANS, Ph.D.**
*U. S. Army Research Institute
of Environmental Medicine
Natick, Massachusetts*

*and*

**NATHAN S. KLINE, M.D.**
*Research Center
Rockland State Hospital
Orangeburg, New York*

**CHARLES C THOMAS** • **PUBLISHER**
*Springfield* • *Illinois* • *U.S.A.*

*Published and Distributed Throughout the World by*
CHARLES C THOMAS • PUBLISHER

BANNERSTONE HOUSE
301-327 East Lawrence Avenue, Springfield, Illinois, U.S.A.
NATCHEZ PLANTATION HOUSE
735 North Atlantic Boulevard, Fort Lauderdale, Florida, U.S.A.

*With* THOMAS BOOKS *careful attention is given to all details of
manufacturing and design. It is the Publisher's desire to present books
that are satisfactory as to their physical qualities and artistic possibilities
and appropriate for their particular use.* THOMAS BOOKS *will be true
to those laws of quality that assure a good name and good will.*

*Printed in the United States of America*
W-2

Published under the Imprimatur

of the

American College of Neuropsychopharmacology

# CONTRIBUTORS

### John Campbell
*Editor, Analog Science Fiction*
*New York, New York*

### Wayne O. Evans, Ph.D.*
*Director, Military Stress Laboratory*
*U. S. Army Research Institute of Environmental Medicine*
*Natick, Massachusetts*

### Stanislav Grof, M.D.
*Chief of Psychiatric Research*
*Maryland Psychiatric Research Center*
*Baltimore, Maryland*

### Martin M. Katz, Ph.D.
*Chief, Clinical Research Branch*
*National Institute of Mental Health*
*Chevy Chase, Maryland*

### Nathan S. Kline, M.D.
*Director, Research Center*
*Rockland State Hospital*
*Orangeburg, New York*

### Arthur Koestler
*Author and Lecturer*
*London, England*

### Albert A. Kurland, M.D.
*Director, Maryland Psychiatric Research Center*
*Baltimore, Maryland*

* "As Author and Editor, the views expressed in this manuscript should not be considered as representing any policy or position of the Department of Defense, but only as the views of a private citizen."

**Heinz E. Lehmann, M.D.**
*Director of Research*
*Douglas Hospital*
*Montreal, Canada*

**Ashley Montagu, Ph.D.**
*Anthropologist and Author*
*Princeton, New Jersey*

**Hon. John Oliver**
*Judge of the Fifth Circuit Court*
*St. Louis, Missouri*

**Walter N. Pahnke, M.D., Ph.D.**
*Director of Clinical Science*
*School of Medicine*
*Johns Hopkins University*
*Baltimore, Maryland*

**Oscar Resnick, Ph.D.**
*Senior Research Scientist*
*Worcester Foundation for Experimental Biology*
*Shrewsbury, Massachusetts*

**Charles Savage, M.D.**
*Associate Director*
*Maryland Psychiatric Research Center*
*Baltimore, Maryland*

**William J. Turner, M.D.**
*Research Psychiatrist*
*Central Islip State Hospital*
*Central Islip, New York*

**Sanford Unger, Ph.D.**
*Chief of Psychological Research*
*Maryland Psychiatric Research Center*
*Baltimore, Maryland*

**Joseph Zubin, Ph.D.**
*Chief, Psychiatric Research, Biometrics Unit*
*New York State Department of Mental Health*
*New York, New York*

To Professor J. E. P. Toman
A teacher, scholar and friend
His untimely death is
A loss to his
Friends and to the Science of
Psychopharmacology

# PREFACE

THE AMERICAN COLLEGE OF NEUROPSYCHOPHARMACOLOGY was
formed in 1961 as a scientific society limited to 150 fellows and
members in which professional information could be exchanged
between pharmacologists, neurophysiologists, psychiatrists, chem-
ists, physicians and psychologists who were active researchers
in the study of mind-altering drugs. Due to the large scale use
of tranquilizers, both in mental hospitals and, also, for outpatients,
it was felt that such an expert body should be assembled for the
purpose of rapid communcation of scientific information. The
College's membership composition reflected the interdisciplinary
nature of the study of mind-altering drugs. Certainly, no one
scientific discipline, by itself, could hope to encompass a field
with as many complexities as that offered by the study of these
drugs.

Since 1961 the College has undergone one minor and one
major change: first, it has allowed its membership to increase to
185 of the most active and most expert investigators studying
psychotropic drugs in the United States today; second, it has
begun to change its role from an organization with the sole
purpose of exchanging scientific information to one with a new
sense of social responsibility to act as an information source about
these drugs. This latter move is illustrated by the recent formation of a Public Information Committee under the chairmanship
of Dr. Joel Elkes, Chairman, Department of Psychiatry, Johns
Hopkins University, an expansion of the role of its Ethics
Committee, under the chairmanship of the senior editor, to
include ethical matters pertaining to society at large in relation
to psychotrophic drugs, as well as of internal matters related
to the ethics of mind-altering drug usage and, perhaps most
noteworthy, the formation of a Public Drug Education Committee
under the chairmanship of Dr. Oakley Ray, of Vanderbilt Uni-

versity. These changes reflect the growing realization that chemical substances which can alter mental, emotional, and perceptual processes are a ubiquitous phenomenon of our culture. Yet, careful, nonbiased descriptions of the actions of these drugs are difficult to obtain.

Mind-altering chemicals are the second most often prescribed type of drugs. Also, on a vast scale we consume over-the-counter psychotropic drugs such as aspirin, caffeine, and alcohol. From early morning until late at night advertisements from our communications media constantly flood us and our children with biased information from so-called "experimental" or "clinical" studies as to the efficacy of particular drugs. And, finally, we see the recent sensational publicity given to the illicit use of drugs of various types for recreational and aesthetic purposes by an increasing percentage of our population. It would probably not be an exaggeration to say that 95 per cent of the readers of this volume will, at some time today, take a drug for the specific purpose of changing their mood, mental functioning, or perceptual capacities. Thus, in light of this almost total usage, the College clearly sees that it has a societal duty to communicate its findings, in a language understandable to the intelligent layman, about the physiological, biochemical, and psychological effects of these compounds. Certainly, the College makes no pretense at having the ultimate societal or moral answers to the questions provoked by the massive use of these chemicals, but it does have the responsibility, within its technical expertise, to explain the known scientific data to the public.

The Study Group for the Effects of Psychotropic Drugs on Normal Humans was initiated four years ago. We recognized that normal humans have used drugs as analgesics, diet reducing compounds, sleeping pills, mood elevators, pep pills, and for recreational purposes since the beginning of man. Therefore, we conclude that this type of usage, i.e. nonpsychiatric, is a legitimate subarea of study in the field of mind-altering drugs. The Study Group was not formed initially to consider the problems of drug misuse. Rather, in its origin, it conceived its mission as a consideration of the possibility of enhancing the quality of human life by chemicals, and a review of the effects of these chemicals when prescribed to the nonpsychotic, and possibly nonneurotic, patient treated in a general outpatient clinic or by a private practitioner. An examination of the contents of this volume will show that it is not directed specifically to the question of drug misuse. Other groups within the College have taken this problem as their particular specialty. However, when one considers the absolute number of people who indulge in caffeine, but not LSD; who use aspirin, but would never touch marijuana; or the moderate drinkers, who would react with horror to the suggestion that they are drug users, we can see that this area of study may constitute the largest, single category of drug use in the United States today. The assertion that we are a "pill taking culture" is perhaps an understatement of the true facts when one considers the amounts of the various drug-containing beverages, the "nondrug" drugs and the "over-the-counter" remedies which we buy.

The theme of the Study Group meeting for the year 1967 was "The Use of Psychotropic Agents in the Year 2000 by Normal Humans." At our meeting in Puerto Rico we concluded that the present breadth of drug use may be almost trivial when we compare it to the possible numbers of chemical substances that will be available for the control of selective aspects of man's life in the year 2000. In this effort we were greatly influenced by the reports in *Daedalus* on the year 2000 and the work of the Committee on The Year 2000. Thus, we decided to try to present to the general public a sample of some of the kinds of drugs that we believe we are capable of producing. It was our intent not only to provide knowledge of our technical capacity, but also a brief analysis of possible social effects of this capability. In this endeavor, we were fortunate to have with us the noted anthropologist, Professor Ashley Montagu, John Campbell, editor of *Analog Science Fiction,* Arthur Koestler, distinguished lecturer and author, and the Honorable John Oliver of the Federal Bench. These gentlemen sat patiently, and with great fortitude, through our technical presentations. At the end of our session, these distinguished gentlemen provided a very informative panel discussion on what they conceived to be the potential outcome of the invention of such drugs, an admonition as to how these drugs should be used and what drugs probably should or should not be invented. It was our hope that by bringing together intelligent men from other areas of specialization, we could obtain a better perspective on our own work. We believe that this hope was more than adequately fulfilled by our panelists.

In considering the present volume it is our hope that the reader will not believe this to be an exercise in science fiction. It is well known that the world of fifteen years hence presently exists in the research laboratory of today. Thus, for at least a period of fifteen years, we are not truly guessing. Further, for the last fifteen years of this century, the speculations that were put forth by the group should be considered not as the only possibilities, but rather as a sampling of the types of potency and selectivity of drug action we have every reason to believe can be achieved. In an age when an opiate compound ten thousand times more potent than morphine has been an established reality for over five years, one cannot think of other possibilities of potent, selective drug actions as remote. If anything, as a criticism of the meeting, it would be our impression that the scientists were far too conservative in their ideas, as is usually the case at meetings of experts.

With these few thoughts we shall leave the reader to make up his own mind and stretch his imagination thirty years into the future to see the type of world in which we will live. Whether we live in a Utopia, an anti-Utopia, or muddle along in a pluralistic society is far more up to the intelligent reader than it is to a small group of psychopharmacologists.

The Study Group would particularly like to thank the National Institute of Mental Health for providing a grant to support its activity. The Workshop Meetings, the Study Group Meeting at our Annual Conference and the publication of the volumes produced by the Study Group would not be possible without the generosity, formerly of Dr. Frank Berger of Wallace Laboratories, and presently, of the National Institute of Mental Health, who provided the financial support required.

WAYNE O. EVANS, PH.D.
NATHAN S. KLINE, M.D.

# INTRODUCTION

IF WE WERE ASKED to name the single most important psychological characteristic of our modern age, I am sure that most of us would answer immediately that it is the ubiquitous sense of rapid change. All around we see our technology, our environment, our institutions, and our values subjected to questions, doubt, attack, and flux. Yet, we are told that this process of change is accelerating and that we should expect even greater disruptions in the future. Whether in reality these changes are actually occurring at such a rapid acceleration is difficult to prove objectively. However, there can be no doubt that the firm conviction held by most people that things are changing explosively constitutes the single most pervasive and potent assumption of our society today. This belief, then, is a major determinant of our perceptions and reactions to the world in which we live, work, play, love and wonder.

When most people in a society feel that their world is changing with an alarming rapidity, anxieties develop as the appropriateness of traditional methods, attitudes, goals and beliefs are challenged. To those of us from the "square" generation, the new sexual liberality, loss of clearly defined sexual roles, affluence, freedom, mobility, protests and clothing styles of the younger generation seem to confront us at every turn as constant reminders of the contempt that many of the youth feel for us and for our institutionalized value structures—values we have striven so hard to attain.

From all our information sources, advertisements, books, editorials, periodicals and reviews, we are admonished to change the brands of the products we use, or build new cities, or change our laws, or worry about a new disease. With an aggravating pervasiveness, the communications media shout with an immediacy and urgency of changes going on, not only in our own country, but all over the world. From the podium of technology and the university we hear the mounting voices of scientific "Cassandras" as they enjoin us not to pollute, not to use drugs, not to reproduce, not to litter, not to smoke, not to consume our vital resources and, of course, not to worry. Yet, at the same time, in the name of "Progress," these "technologists" tell us we dare not impede the cumulative growth of an unbridled science and technology or stop a pattern of ever-increasing consumption and discard cycle for fear of "lagging behind' 'or creating un-employment. Our political and military leaders proclaim to us the ever-present threat of the destruction of mankind and of the necessity for our deep involvement in political activities in countries all over the world—due to rapid modes of transportation and the variety of weapons of mass destruction. Yet, they assure us, the parochial, rural morality, individualism and nationalism of our country's colonial period is still our guiding ethic. In our cities we see the changes brought about by the mass society with its production of mass, "mediocre" culture, and we accept, with a minimum of complaint, the ever-lengthening queues in which we must stand to obtain even the simplest services. In the most unchanging of all our organizations, the church—the earthly representation of our "eternal" spiritual life—we see vast up-heavals of faith and ritual. It is difficult to conceive of any time in history since the Protestant Reformation when a "Folk" Mass could be accepted or in which "love-ins" and "feel-ins" could be conducted in strict, Protestant Churches. The "new" church has moved to the suburbs and become an institutional mirror image of its members.

The effect of this overwhelming advertising campaign of change has been to produce a constant state of anxiety in many people and total alienation in some. We no longer know where to turn or whom to ask to obtain sincere answers to questions of identity and goals. When "God dies" lesser authority figures suffer an even worse fate—disbelief or disregard. In a "screaming" society, the quiet voice of reason is unheard. The deeds and goals of our past appear meaningless when applied to the future and the increasing specialization of information robs us of any hope of understanding our universe from a human perspective.

One of the least insane responses to the feeling of anxiety induced by our perception of a world in flux has been the re-institution of Utopian thought. After a hiatus of over fifty years, the Utopian mode of thinking again has come to the fore and, with it, the proclamation of new goals, new men and new social orders, as envisioned by the authors of the Utopias—each contending that he (or she) will give a sense of order, meaning and stability to our lives. Prophets abound and we have to learn to be leary of "Learys."

One of the most interesting forms of the new Utopian thought is the emergence of the "futurologists." Intellectuals of the standing of Daniel Bell of Columbia University, Herman Kahn of the Hudson Institute and Bertrand de Jouvenel, leader of the Futuribles Project in France, have brought together a mixture of simple, extrapolatory projections, methods from operations research, Delphic "scenarios" of multifold trends, sociologic diffusion models, and some straightforward evaluative prejudices to produce quasi-scientific techniques which supposedly allow us to examine the possible, alternative world futures resulting from our present actions. By these methods, we are given, at least, the impression that we can exercise some willful control over our destiny and thus retain some degree of personal stability and integrity in a world of frantic change. Whether any of these various methods actually will predict the future is yet to be seen, but there can be no doubt that they do provide the reader (and the predictor) a feeling of psychological security by establishing a methodology which purports to determine the long-range consequences of our actions in a nonstatic environment. In a sense, these dynamic techniques have replaced the Utopian concepts of the past which emphasized stable societal institutions. We now seek societal stability by institutionalizing the process of change itself.

> "The *Method* is the thing to catch the fancy of
> the *Scientist-King*"
> (With apologies
> to Shakespeare
> W.O.E.)

Personal stability is gained by placing our faith in a method which analyzes change itself. Differential equations of rate change have replaced the static rituals of past institutions, and stochastic models have replaced sacrifices to appease the modern "computor" gods. We are forced to make the process of change orderly in order to insure our own psychological well-being. For generations historical and sociological theorists sought a model of social change without success. Yet, now our need has produced a faith in prediction validity of these untested methods.

Unfortunately, such esoteric models of change are only of use as "tranquilizers" or "pacifiers" to a few, highly educated members of our society. These few, however, are in a position to produce a self-fulfilling prophecy by their ability to implement changes in governmental funding policies and to attract public notoriety to help validate the prophecy. It is interesting, and somewhat frightening, to conceive of an age of orderly, programmed change in which random creativity becomes a threat to "The Plan." We can imagine the reverent, servile dedication with which clerks will input the latest social survey data to be displayed after analysis on a master PERT board to indicate the progress of "The Plan"; the sincerity with which "The Plan's" implementors will pronounce Galbraithian dictums of a neo-post-industrial economy, and the horror and chastisement that might greet any layman so bold as to challenge the accuracy, the necessity, or the desirability of the particular future expressed by "The Plan." Orthodoxy may come to be the humble acceptance of an approved social change equation. Certainly no drug effect, no matter how "mind-expanding," can begin to approach in scope or folly the boundless, righteous ego of a man who has accepted a "doctrine" to justify himself with a sense of purpose and meaning.

Psychotropic drugs do have something in common with the new Utopian thought—both may provide a sense of stability and certainty, whether realistic or not, and reduce the feeling of chaos generated by a perceived social flux. Social planners well might consider the description of long-range forecasting as a "tranquilizer" for reformers. Tranquility is not always a state with a high survival potential, nor is orthodoxy adaptable in a world of changing problems.

Psychotropic drugs have become of concern to our society because of their sudden popularization. Chemicals which could alter the state of mind or mood have been administered by physicians, witch doctors, priests, medicine men, or by self-medication throughout history and in almost every culture. As far back as the Vedas of ancient India we find reference to the drug Soma as having both mystical and palliative properties. Alcohol was described by the Egyptians as being given to men by Osiris to relieve the troubles of their lives. Kava Kava has been used by the natives in the Samoan Island group for its mental effects, and the Indians of South America have been relatively fortunate in the multitude of alkaloid bearing plants which they can take to induce a change in their mental functioning. However, the explosion of mind or mood altering drugs in this country started in the year 1955, when a small group of dedicated, radical thinking young psychiatrists introduced tranquilizing drugs into the state mental hospitals of our country. This was accomplished almost without the knowledge of the predominantly psychoanalytically-oriented psychiatric establishment. The results of the introduction of these drugs were so dramatic that only the most fervent disbelievers could hold out against the onslaught of data. The use of these chemicals has reversed the curve of ever-increasing numbers of mental patients in our state hospitals. At this time, the curve is on a rapid downward path.

Due to the realization of the medicinal benefits of chemicals for the relief of certain types of mental illness, major efforts were initiated by the pharmaceutical industry to look for new chemical substances which would have mind-altering properties. Further, the military-industrial *symbiants* began to sponsor projects to produce chemicals which could disrupt the will of an enemy to fight without damaging his body. This latter effort was designed both to wage more humanitarian wars and, also, for use in situations in which the hostile elements of a population were intermingled with neutral and friendly elements—the situation most usually found in conditions of insurgency. Also, intense investigation of the use of natural products by various peoples all over the world was instituted in the hope of discovering new products.

The munificent results of these intensive research efforts are now seen in our pill-taking culture with a drug of choice for all ages: antidepressants for the elderly, tranquilizers for the middle aged, alcohol and pep pills for the young adult, and "mind-expanders" for the youth. From morning until night there are advertisements from the mass media, attention arousing condemnations from local police, prescriptions from family physicians, and word of mouth advice from peers emphasizing that "such-and-such" a chemical will help with whatever problem a person might have, such as pain, insomnia, boredom, lethargia, anxiety, etc. Psychomedication is an accepted way of life and the search for the "just right" pill has become the existential goal for many people and a habitual consideration for the rest of us.

The present volume can be regarded as a "tranquilizer" for psychopharmacologists, that is, people who discover and study mind-altering drugs. Those of us who work in this field see a developing potential for nearly a total control of human emotional status, mental functioning, and will to act. These human phenomena can be started, stopped or eliminated by the use of various types of chemical substances. What we can produce with our science now will affect the entire society. In a sense, we are in the same ethical and moral dilemma as the physicists in the days prior to the Manhattan Project. Our tradition and allegiance to the ethos of science and technology makes us feel the responsibility to explore every lead which may produce new chemicals which can help, or control, man. On the other hand, we obviously see the possibilities for social stagnation or repression when such agents are perfected. Along with the geneticists, with their near ability to modify human genetic potential, we are participating in the development of what can be called a "biological atom bomb." For this reason a group of us have come together to inform the intelligent, lay public of the kinds of drugs we are capable of producing. Although this disclosure may not result in a wise use of psychochemicals in the future, at least we will feel that we can share part of our concern and guilt with the general public. If drugs are invented and used in ways which are not beneficial to mankind, psychopharmacologists will not be exempted from the disaster. Therefore, we ask you, the intelligent public, to help us answer the following questions.

1. What drugs should be invented and when?
2. Who should control drug production and use? What control means should be used?
3. How free should people be allowed to be in regard to drug use?
4. How can effective education about drug use be implemented?
5. What limits must be placed on governmental use of drugs to control individuals?
6. *Where does freedom of research end and public responsibility begin?*

WAYNE O. EVANS, PH.D.

# CONTENTS

# PSYCHOTROPIC DRUGS IN THE YEAR 2000
## Use By Normal Humans

# 1

## THE ETIOLOGY OF BEHAVIOR IN THE YEAR 2,000

JOSEPH ZUBIN

I HAVE CHOSEN AS my topic the etiology or general underlying causes of behavior in the year 2,000 in order to provide an introduction to the papers that will follow which deal with the specific impact of drugs on behavior. In a sense I am to provide the baselines on which drugs will be superimposed.

Had I foreseen the task in September as fully as I see it now, I would probably not have undertaken it. As a matter of fact, psychology, the science of behavior, has only recently begun to consider causes. Most of its last one hundred years have been spent in studying and classifying the effect of these causes—behavior itself, i.e. the response side of the problem rather than the stimulus. Indeed, the search for the stimulus, or cause of behavior, is one of the major unsolved problems facing psychology. *Cherchez la cause* is the chief concern of most students of behavior today.

Why should the search for the cause be so important? Why not study the more palpable response per se, and note how it is altered by drugs and leave cause to philosophy? The reason for studying cause is that the number of ways in which behavioral responses may vary is rather limited, while the number of causes that may bring them about it manifold. Whether this is basically true or is only apparently true, because we have already developed a taxonomy of responses but do not yet have a good taxonomy of causes, remains an open question. Perhaps the bewildering array of causes may some day yield as neat a pattern of categories as we have found for the responses. But that day is not yet here.

3

In looking for the sources of behavior, we are faced with a tremendous number of bewildering options. We could look for physical, physiological, instinctual (play, curiosity, etc.), social, cultural, or philosophical causes, to name only a few.

Since we do not have any basic knowledge of the causes of behavior, all we can do now is develop ideal etiologies in the form of scientific models which would give us the structures from which to draw our hypotheses concerning underlying causes.

There is no need for a defense of scientific models; nevertheless, the imaginative schemas, built first on fantasy, which underlie the structure of models and which are either vindicated or rejected by actual observation, are most succinctly illustrated in the following episode.

> When Robert Boyle died in 1691, Christian Huygens and Gottfried Wilhelm von Leibnitz commiserated that he had wasted his talents trying to prove by *experiments* what they knew to be true in the light of *reason*—that he was more interested in *observation* than in *reasoning* and had left no unified body of thought. (Hall, 1967.)

This conflict between schemas based on mere speculative reasoning and crass empiricism based on a plethora of observations is resolved through the scientific model, which combines schematization with the built-in mechanism for testing the hypotheses arising from the schema through observation and experiment.

In searching for a group of scientific models that might be useful in explaining human behavior, the following come to mind: (a) the ecological model, according to which the sources of man's behavior are to be found in the social-cultural or ecological niche which he occupies; (b) the developmental model, according to which the source of man's behavior can be attributed to the variety of the developmental crises (critical periods) through which he passes and the proper or improper satisfaction of needs at these junctures that may lead him in the direction of good or poor development; (c) the learning and conditioning model, which stipulates that man's behavior is primarily the resultant of the particular kinds and schedules of reinforcement which he has been subjected to; (d) the genetic model, which stipulates

that man's behavior is primarily reducible to the genetic endowment with which he comes into the world; (e) the internal environment model, which stipulates that the body fluids and body chemistry are the chief bases of man's behavior; and (f) the neurophysiological model, which stipulates that the etiology of man's behavior is to be sought in his neurophysiological equipment, especially the central nervous system. I have elsewhere (Zubin, 1966) applied these scientific models to the explanation of etiology of mental disorders, but it is high time that a similar system of models be applied to normal development.

There is one difficulty in all of this classification, and that arises from the essential fact that the classification of ignorance is always very difficult! But where our knowledge ends, our freedom to speculate or roam in the explanatory area is, of course, unlimited. Speculation is all that we can engage in at this point; nevertheless, controlled speculation may show the way for the type of research required for producing a classificatory system of causes of behavior that would be of value. Besides, the speculation or fantasy of today is the reality of tomorrow, and the reality of today is nothing more than the legend of the day after tomorrow.

While these models are conceived of as independent for heuristic purposes, they are in reality interdependent to a greater or lesser degree. This interrelationship is indicated in the diagram. The ecological model and the learning model refer primarily to the exogeneous factors impinging on the individual. The develop-

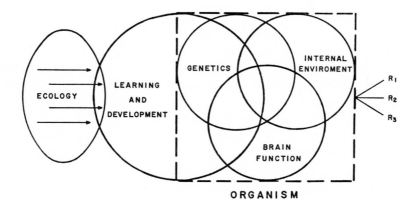

ORGANISM

mental model is partly exogeneous, influenced by ecological and learning factors and partly endogeneous, reflecting maturation. The genetic, internal environment and the neurophysiological models operate entirely within the skin, but they are mutually interrelated as well as influenced by the ecological forces by learning and development.

We shall now take up each of the models in turn, describing its assumptions, and the causal agent presumably salient to it.

For heuristic purposes we deal one at a time with causal factors of the model under discussion, assuming that the factors assigned to the other models are not also involved in the behavior under examination. Thus, when we deal with the ecological model we will assume that it alone is responsible for the particular behavior and that the basic capacity involved in development, learning, genetic expression, internal environment and neurophysiology is essentially intact or normal and not contributing to the deviant behavior. This is a simplifying assumption, which of course will be corrected later.

The human ecology model is built on the assumption that human behavior is directly attributable to the particular factors operating in the ecological niche in which the individual finds himself. The evidence for social-cultural, environmental pressures as etiological agents in behavior comes largely from studies of socioeconomic status, isolation, educational and social deprivation, and social-cultural change due to migration or rapid acculturation which affect behavior adversely through some such general factor as stress and stratification of society. The evidence for more benign factors affecting behavior positively is not as available nor as convincing. However, even the most sanguine environmentalist will not be satisfied with merely indicating the above mentioned factors as causal agents and will try to determine just how these forces bring about salutary or deleterious effects.

To cope with the stimuli assumed to operate under this model, we need techniques and methods that will delineate the various environmental forces that underlie the production of behavior. Our handicap here is tremendous because even preliminary descriptive work is yet to be done. We do not have a taxonomy of ecological factors that is suitable for the exploration of behavior, nor do we know the links between these global forces and the proximate forms by which they may bring about a given type of behavior. It is of course true that social science has developed a number of sophisticated taxonomies in what I am calling the "human ecology" realm. We have classification systems for economic modes, social organization, kinship, cultural complexity and so on. But in relating behavior to these we generate a rather frightening plethora of "intervening variables"; conspicuously we lack parametric control. For example, in face of the often demonstrated fact that the prevalence rates of major psychiatric disorders are quite constant across cultures, we find ourselves invoking such constructs as "individual stress" or "personality" to explain differences between the subgroups that constitute a given culture. These may be just the right middle level construct—they may pay off. But we will not know until they can be anchored objectively and measured either in the casual or consequential realm. If indeed such constructs can be objectified, we may find that the more molar taxonomy will no longer serve our purpose.

Recent work by Richard Wolf (1965) illustrated how the correlation between social status and intelligence, which is usually found to be between 0.20 and 0.40, can be boosted to as high as 0.69 if the parameters of the socioeconomic environment that have a bearing on intellectual potential are measured and included in the multiple correlation. Similarly, the correlation between social status and achievement, which is usually found to be 0.50, can rise to 0.80 if the parameters of social status pertinent to achievement are identified and measured. How the factors presumably underlying low socioeconomic status will relate to the occurrence of psychopathology when their parameters are explicated and measured no one can tell, but arguments such as those provided by Bruce P. Dohrenwend (1965) lead one to suppose that at least transient, if not permanent, psychopathology is highly related to the stresses and strains of the environment. Perhaps persistent noxious stress can even lead to permanent psychopathology.

The developmental model of etiology of behavior is built on the assumption that mental disease develops as a result of some specific deprivation or interference during a critical period in development when that specific deficit or interference is crucial. A general underlying factor in this model is the aging process itself with the growth and decline of function that it entails. Identification of the critical periods of development is still moot, with research covering the entire ontogenetic range: fetal, neonatal, childhood, adolescence, adulthood, middle-age and old-age. Moreover, the values of the variables that may affect behavior at the critical junctures are still to be specified. At present, such obvious factors as absence of toxemia during the gestation period, rich early experience, sufficient interaction with peers during early childhood and adolescence, good psychosexual development and good vocational adjustment patterns, satisfactory role development in family, vocation and society, and social interaction in old-age can be tabulated as important causal agents in the direction of good development. How to measure the degree of well-being during pregnancy, the extent of peer relationship, the pattern of friendship, and so forth, is still beyond us. Even the categorization of family interaction in terms of degree of relationship between its members shows no universal agreement. But it is interesting to note that there is far more done in the area of deviant behavior in these respects than in the area of normative behavior.

As an example of the study of one of the developmental parameters we might examine peer relationships during early development. Harlow (1962) has demonstrated that macaque monkeys raised without peer interaction tend to develop rather poorly, especially with reference to psychosexual development. Investigation of the adolescent friendship patterns of preschizophrenic adolescents (Kreisman, 1967) indicates that compared to normals their adolescent friendship pattern is quite deviant. Whether this represents an etiological factor in schizophrenia, or, whether it indicates subclinical schizophrenia is, of course, difficult to determine.

Here again, we must have independent measures of parameters of the environment that are still unidentified. Meantime, we can point to some of the behaviors that seem to be direct reflections of good or poor development: linguistic or verbal behavior, comprehensibility of speech, greeting, eating, sleeping, and other types of daily behavior accompanying socialization.

One of the more exciting developmental studies is that of Papoušek in Prague, Czechoslovakia at the Institute for the Care of Mother and Child. (Papoušek, 1968). Here the neonates are placed under more or less similar social environments from birth on, so that social-cultural determinants as a source of individual differences are largely eliminated. Care is taken to include only healthy infants without any evidence of pathology in pregnancy or in delivery, and they are reared in a special unit under relatively standard conditions with the assistance of mothers and specially trained nurses who can substitute for mothers if necessary. Despite this uniformity of environmental conditions striking differences in conditionability emerge. Whether this is to be attributed to primarily genetic factors or developmental-learning factors is still an open issue.

Finally, it should be pointed out that certain kinds of developmental models may be considered as special cases of the ecological model. In a model, for example, which postulates family structure, e.g. broken homes, as crucial for the development of psychopathology, what is really being suggested is that childhood is an optimal period for *transmitting* certain effects from the social-cultural environment to the individual. Such a conceptualization may lead one to consider the role of learning in relation to psychopathology.

The learning or conditioning model postulates that the source of the normal or deviant behavior of the patient is to be sought in his reinforcement history and the current behavior-reinforcement contingencies.

The learning model has one underlying component viz.— reinforcement—which may serve the function of selecting for survival those behaviors in the inborn repertoire of the neonate which are most essential for his continued development. In this way, reinforcement may serve the same function for selective survival of behaviors and their shaping that evolution serves in selection for survival of species and their adaptation. Because learning is dependent on innate mechanisms like sensory analyzers and unconditioned responses, it is difficult to separate the learning process from them, but for heuristic purposes we shall assume these underlying mechanisms not to be deviant to begin with and discuss only the normative development or maldevelopment due to the learning process itself.

It seems reasonable to assume that many behavior deviations, especially in the neuroses and other nonorganic conditions, must be acquired in accordance with known learning principles or with those which are still to be discovered. The learning procedures, intentional or unintentional, that our culture utilizes in shaping behavior are gradually becoming known. Some of the basic principles (such as schedules of reinforcement) have been studied extensively in animals and are beginning to be applied to human beings, especially in the area of verbal and other social behavior. The acquisition of adaptive emotional responses, however, is still largely to be investigated in humans. In general, the parameters of the learning process itself are slowly revealing themselves, since the products of such learning, whatever the process may consist of, are easily observable and often measurable.

The physical basis of learning also may cast light on normative as well as deviational possibilities. The identification of biochemical processes involved in consolidation, and the finding that certain stimulants injected after a learning episode can exert a retrograde facilitation effect that shows up after the drug has worn off, has potentialities for perhaps reducing the difference between learning by retardates and by normals. Similarly, the role of attention (perhaps conceived of as involving nervous-system "efficiency") in learning of both retardates and schizophrenics has been investigated; according to Zeaman and House (1963), one reason why retardates of certain levels fail to learn quickly is the long trial-and-error period before they select the proper stimulus to attend to.

Further illustrating the possibility of interaction between models, a study by Salzinger and colleagues (1961) demonstrated that the administration of chlorpromazine affected only that class of behavior that was being reinforced. When verbal behavior in general was being reinforced it was emitted at a lower rate than when no drug was administered. On the other hand, when self-referred affect statements were being reinforced only these showed a lower rate of emission, speech level remaining the same. Finally, when movement in the subject's chair was measured (another response class not under the reinforcement contingency), it showed, if anything, a higher rate owing to the administration of the tranquilizer. It was therefore concluded based on a couple of subjects that the effect of the drug was not directly upon the behavior, but was indirect, perhaps through some aspect of the reinforcement process.

Another consideration in the etiology of deviant behavior is the status of the original stimulus in producing the deviant behavior—the role of traumatic events, for example, as distinct from the factors maintaining the behavior long after the effect of the initial stimulus has disappeared. The contingencies of reinforcement for specific deviant behavior may serve to maintain it, whether the reinforcement is intended or not. Similar contingencies are to be sought in the maintenance of normal behavior.

With regard to measuring the deviation in behavior referrable to learning, the entire gamut of patient behavior is involved; much of it can be observed in the clinic and hospital, and some of it measured under laboratory situations. Here, observational techniques and interviewing under individual or group conditions are available, but standard procedures for the assessment of degree of psychopathology in relation to learning principles are only beginning to be provided on a practical basis (Kanfer and Saslow, 1965).

It might be pointed out here that learned behavior, as a basis for causation, detection, diagnosis, and elimination of psychopathology has received a new impetus from some of the successes reported for behavior therapy. No one can deny that, at least at the present time, there is no other way to detect the presence of functional psychopathology except through overt behavior, verbal or nonverbal. But it must also be realized that the same behavior may receive positive reinforcement in one culture, negative in another, and be completely ignored in a third. This fact may lead us to adopt either a purely relativistic view on mental disorders or to search for other indicators which may accompany or underlie the pathology. The learning theorists for the most part object to this, saying that the behavior and its functional relationship to the environment is the psychopathology and nothing else is needed. Yet, if we discover that a neonate is incapable of some metabolic process (say metabolism of phenylalanine) and neglect it, because the neonate is not demonstrating any pathological behavior, we may lose the opportunity of saving him from mental retardation later. It is in this sense that we should be critical of the statement that we need to pay attention only to current behavior, unless we wish to include all activity of the organism, even the cellular or segmental, as behavior. In this way, a thorough survey of the various response systems of patients, besides their overt behavior, may permit the detection and diagnosis of even latent conditions that have not yet come to function in addition to providing a more objective indicator of the presence of the illness.

The genetic model postulates that, as far as psychopathology is concerned, the basic origin of mental deviation is an inherited propensity. The investigation of the parameters of normal heredity is hardly begun, though those underlying deviant heredity are gradually becoming known. The genetic origins of some types of mental disorders can be demonstrated in the form of certain inborn errors of metabolism, as in PKU or galactosemia, or can be associated with specific chromosome anomalies, as in mongolism, or can be inferred from studies of consanguinity ranging from absence of any blood relatedness to monozygocity. Comparing hereditary factors with social-cultural factors, it is clear that we have today a better measure of hereditary similarity in the degree of consanguinity than we have of environmental similarity. The relationship between degree of consanguinity and resemblance in IQ is quite linear and positive. The relationship between resemblance in environmental factors and resemblance in IQ is practically zero (Jarvik and Erlenmeyer-Kimling, 1967). But this may be a reflection of the fact that we have good measures of hereditary resemblance but few good measures of environmental resemblance. Indeed, the genetic stimuli that give rise to deviant behavior have been detected and described in much better fashion than the environmental factors or the factors underlying any of the other models that may account for deviation. Among the genetic factors leading to mental deviation are some identifiable genetic anomalies, such as translocation and nondisjunction as evidence in Down's Syndrome, mosaics, and specific alleles or combination of alleles that because of their enzymatic activity interfere with normal cell development and functioning. Some of the other genetic principles that have been employed in etiological considerations are polymorphism (or the balance maintained between alternative genic structures in given internal or external environments), penetrance and expressivity of genes.

There has been a recent flurry of interest in the potential evolutionary survival value of such disorders as schizophrenia. One recent suggestion is that the genetic element in schizophrenia has something to do with the unpredictability of schizophrenic behavior when viewed from the standpoint of normative expectancy. This unpredictable behavior may be valued highly if it meets with social acceptance and is rewarded by society, or may be rejected and classified as illness (Hammer and Zubin, 1968).

Genetics may be viewed in terms of biochemical mechanisms by which the genes serve as precursors for the production of certain enzymes whose absence (or excess) prevents the organism from prospering. There is, therefore, considerable hope that an investigation of the internal environment of the body may reveal the particular metabolic deficiency or excess that characterizes the patient. A particular error of metabolism may, of course, be inherited or acquired. A considerable amount of effort has been spent in the attempt to relate schizophrenia to metabolic error. Certain fractions of schizophrenic blood have produced metabolic alterations as well as changes in such behaviors as rope-climbing in rats, as well as transitory changes in the psychomotor behavior of normal human subjects. Presumably similar fractions from the blood of normals do not produce such changes. The parametric studies of serology, chromosomal counts, etc., may turn out to be important bases for classification either with or without immediate behavioral correlates.

The specific aspects of the internal environment, such as

homeostasis, endocrine balance, acid-base balance, electrolyte metabolism (Coppen, 1967) and other internal mechanisms and circulating fluids are too many to mention, but there is again a need for classifying them into stimulus class that may be useful in relating them to behavior. Considerable advances have been made in the analysis of serum protein and hemaglobin, enzymes, bile salts, antigens, etc., which may prove useful in classification. Similarly, Hamburg *et al.* (Hamburg, 1967) have reviewed thyroid function in relation to genetics and the rest of the internal environment with special reference to behavior and pointed out many new leads. Here again the mediation of factors operating in other models, such as the genetic or the neuro-physiological, is important.

The final model, the neurophysiological or brain-function model, postulates that human behavior depends basically on neurophysiological control especially through the central nervous system, and that the function of the brain is to organize and control behavior in all its aspects from the physiological to the conceptual levels. Some years ago I developed a table in which the various aspects of behavior—physiological, sensory, perceptual, psychomotor and conceptual were classified against the various methods for eliciting them under laboratory conditions: idling state, energy stimuli and signal stimuli (Burdock, Sutton, and Zubin, 1958). This constituted a sort of Mendelejeff Table for psychological experimentation.

Not only normal but also abnormal behavior is dependent upon the functioning or malfunctioning of the organ that most directly controls behavior—the brain. The nature of this mal-functioning can only be guessed at, but certain behavioral characteristics have been found in some types of mental disorder that differentiate patients from normals in a way that seems to be independent of ecological factors and that presumably reflects brain function (either innately, by endowment, or in the course of ontogeny). For example, slower recovery of evoked potentials to rapidly succeeding stimuli, and slower reaction time when a stimulus modality shift occurs, have been found. The actual brain substrates or processes underlying these deviations are still to be discovered. Except for certain "textbook" neurological syndromes, we probably know less about neurophysio-logical factors for the production of deviant behavior than we know about factors or stimuli in any of the other models (except, perhaps, for the internal-environment model).

Nevertheless, some of the aspects of brain structure and function that have been implicated in the production of deviant behavior are amount of endogeneous neural noise, general level of arousal, reticular activating system, limbic lobe, temporal lobe, hippocampus and amygdala, peripheral gating mechanisms for dealing with excessive or diminished inputs, reverberating circuits, and the general integrative capacities of the cortex.

So much for the current scene. Now, what about the year 2,000? What will be the basic causes of behavior and how will the parameters of the causal factors underlying each of the models be altered?

The future of psychopathology was delineated in a symposium of the American Psychopathological Association some seven years ago (Hoch and Zubin, 1962). With the more limited scope of psychopathology it was somewhat easier to look ahead and focus on such issues as the future of each of the etiological models, but even here the editors took refuge in their preface in the following:

> The experience of other disciplines indicates that even un-successful predictions can be of use. Why a prediction went wrong and where it went wrong and under what circumstances may be illuminating. Attempts at explaining unanticipated unsuccessful thera-peutic outcomes or unanticipated successes can throw more light on the therapeutic process than can demonstrations of expected success-ful therapeutic effort . . . we hope that the next generation will find these predictions entertaining as well as instructive—regardless of whether or not our prediction will prove right or wrong.

Our attempts to predict the future of the sources of behavior is even more hazardous, but in the light of the above comments our venture into prophecy may be forgiven.

In the matter of prediction, to paraphrase Goethe, who can say something clever or something stupid that has not been said before? If there is any virtue in what I am about to say, it inheres not in the novelty of my ideas but in the new organization I impose on the material, reshuffling the deck so as to permit the emergence of new sequences that may not have been observed before. But there is another reason—truth and the search for truth can be suppressed not only by ill will but also by good will (Stern, 1967). Proposals for innovations have often been withheld not by ill will, but by the fear that they may entail some harm as well as benefit. How often have we heard that basic research only breeds more questions, and we already have enough questions? How often have we been told that blind science can only bring self-destruction? We must realize that beginning with Prometheus' bringing fire and ending with the discovery of nuclear power, innovations have brought benefits as well as destruction. We can not hold back science until man becomes fully moral any more than we can withhold the stars from view until the last pagan worshipper dies off.

Let us begin with the ecological model. Here, rightly or wrongly, the architects have made the greatest dent. Someone has said that surgeons bury their mistakes, psychiatrists hospitalize them, while architects have to live in them! Maybe that is why the architects are so concerned with the future. But unlike other professions, whom Shaw has accused of being conspiracies against the laity, architects have opened up their offices and ideas to colleagues in other fields as demonstrated by the avalanche of books and articles on architecture and the social sciences. In his summary of a book reporting a conference of architects, social scientists, planners, philosophers and historians, Anderson (1968) points out that in view of the complexity of the situation, it is impossible to predict changes, but we can instead map out some of the multiple possibilities that may be placed before man in making his choices. This is the path I will follow.

Let us raise the first issue regarding the making of these choices. Who will be making them? It appears that the leisure class, which today constitutes a wealthy minority, will in the year 2,000 probably constitute a democratic majority and the choice will be largely in its hands. How these choices are to be made, the criteria on which they are to be made, will depend on the prevalent value system of the day. Right and wrong are not absolute but heavily dependent on the sense of values that prevail.

One of the sources of man's behavior seems to be activity for the sake of activity itself—the kind of activity which one engages in during his leisure time.

If we define leisure activity as anything not done for the sake of something else, but for its own sake, we can revive for the year 2,000 one of the mainspring of man's activity, the play tendency, a mainspring to which Huisinga (1950) has devoted an entire volume. He points out that the play tendency which underlies leisure is fundamental in man's development, that it is the one avenue through which man can free himself from sordid reality and dwell in a regulating well-ordered fantasy life; that it is the source of ritual and eventually of law, and is also the basis for friendship.

The question immediately arises whether this leisure may not lead to boredom. There is a conflict between our Puritan work ethic and leisure, which the historian Tillinghast traces as follows (in Anderson, 1968):

> In primitive societies the pattern of work and leisure was seasonal and tradition-directed, and few choices were necessary; ritual and inherited status patterns kept the tribe together. Later came the great invention of slavery, which made leisure in the modern sense possible for the ruling class. In the Greek world the arts, sciences, and intellect in general developed astonishingly. Few people had leisure, but those who did used it gorgeously. In Rome, on the other hand, the same institution (slavery-based leisure) had a different outcome: growing restlessness and boredom, and as the Empire developed, bread and circuses for the unemployed.
>
> By the thirteenth century, European slaves had usually become serfs, but the cultured class still believed in contemplation, which, like everything else, was worked out by the principles of scholastic philosophy. Among other scholastic products was an analysis of the problem of leisure, although it was not called that. The medieval ethic was not based on the righteousness of work, except for the lower classes; work was the curse of Adam. The highest good was not action to improve society, but contemplation of God in solitude. But in contemplative communities certain problems arose. A serious one was *accidie*, the noonday demon, the terror of medieval abbots. Accidie or acedia was a kind of cosmic boredom, sometimes leading

to despair and ultimately to suicide and Hell; its translation was sloth. The point is that economic idleness itself was not regarded as evil, but only the things it led to when it was poorly used. Thus sloth had no connection with leisure; it was not the thing that made leisure possible but that which made it impossible.

. . . All late civilizations—for example the Hellenistic world and the fifteenth century in northern Europe—have a cult of melancholy. But whereas before it was always aristocratic, today it reaches all sections of society . . .

and as leisure increases even more it may become one of our major problems. Whether it will be possible to counteract the "accidie" or sloth of the future with drugs remains an interesting question.

Granted that one of the problems of the year 2,000 arises from the multiplicity of available choices, working out the consequences of each choice would involve a stupendous expenditure, but probably no greater than that now devoted to the planning of wars that will never be fought which occupies the Pentagon.

Another ecological issue we might raise is whether it will be necessary to permit cities to grow beyond the point where they cease to confer a net advantage upon the inhabitants and instead produce slums and ghettos. Similar questions have been raised regarding such institutions as hospitals, schools, prisons, etc. Investigations of animal populations have indicated that animals require a minimum private space below which trouble starts. If the crowding reduces the available space below the minimum, an automatic reduction in population takes place through killings, mass suicide, disruption of courting and of mating patterns, of nest building and of care of the young. Aggression and fighting increase, sexual conduct becomes more "sadistic," and there is an increase in circulatory and heart disease. Just how overcrowding brings about these effects is still an open question, and the effect of overcrowding on the internal environment is one of the problems of the future.

The general factor of temporal change in social and environmental factors will have to be recognized. The dematerialization and deterioration and destruction processes of the environment seem to be well on their way already. The possible disappearance of the institutions that served mankind in the twentieth century, church and family, and the lack of suitable substitutes may create sources of maladaptive behavior at least during the transition to new forms.*

Turning to the developmental model, it is quite clear that early infant experience is beginning to be recognized as one of the fundamental bases for subsequent personality. Anyone who has watched the feeding of a neonate, as Dr. Daniel Stern at the Psychiatric Institute is beginning to do through the help of videotapes, is impressed by the powerful thrust of reinforcement provided by the feeding interaction between mother and child. Feeding is probably the strongest reinforcer we have, and it reinforces not only sucking behvaior but any antecedent or concomitant behavior that may be ongoing. Crying, temper tantrums, quiet play or any other types of behavior displayed by the child are all reinforced powerfully by means of feeding, and one wonders whether the control of such powerful forces should be left to amateurs. Let us suppose for a moment that breathing were to be placed under contingency control. Think how easily even deeply engrained behaviors could be eliminated (as was done to some extent with alcoholics in Canada) through negative reinforcement or how new behaviors could be introduced through positive reinforcement. Feeding may be as powerful, though not so dramatically life threatening, as breathing.

Would it not be better to train mothers to become experts in learning theory and guide their behavior along learning theory principles during feeding? Or, perhaps, the whole feeding procedure because of its delicate nature can be reduced in importance by automated schedules of reinforcement. If this were so, we would have another baseline for measuring effects of drugs!

The mothers, instead of fumbling with feeding could spend their time with speech development or with less potent reinforcers such as satisfying curiosity, arranging for playfulness, and other activities that now go unrewarded. Perhaps the day will come

_____

* The nature of the transitional state is illustrated by the following story. An anthropologist asked an old brave on an Indian Reservation whether he would be willing to spend a night sleeping in the cemetery. The old brave agreed, saying he would spread his holy beans around him and sleep like a pig. The young brave refused the request. Why? He had lost faith in the beans and as yet found no replacement!

when mothers will be no more prone to feed their babies than doctors are to treat their own families, but I better postpone this to the year 3,000.

In the area of the learning model, schools and colleges may be abolished and substituted by television monitors and storage retrieval mechanisms. The status of student will be abolished and instead people will learn while they work or while engaged in leisure activity in accordance with their felt needs. Thus, instead of having youth isolated behind ivy-clad walls, they will be returned to their families (even as is now the case with mental patients) and alienation of youth may become a thing of the past.

As a result of the revolution in education, a better understanding of the self will be attained. The studies of personality and vocational choice which were based on random samples and selected variables during the twentieth century will become passé. Instead, single individual studies only will be conducted in which the subject, because of his self-knowledge, could provide *a priori* Bayesian probabilities in experiments, and Bayesian statistics will replace classical statistics.

For the genetic model, in order to reduce the reproduction of the palpably unfit, mothers who are found to be carriers will be rewarded each month they remain nonpregnant by immediate monetary rewards. New classification systems based on genetic characteristics will help in prediction of behavior.

Physiological age will become as common and popular a concept as chronological or mental age is today. The comparison of drug effects will become easier when physiological age is used as a standard.

For the internal environment model, new classification of humans will emerge from the classification of responsiveness to a variety of drugs. Knowledge of autoimmunity will become an important force in postponing decrepitude in aging and possibly extend man's span of life. Better knowledge of nutrition, gained from experimentation in backward countries with diet deficient populations, will enable us to insure proper diet not only for the general population but especially for leaders in making decisions.

At the present time, classification of human behavior is based either on self-reporting inventories, psychological performance tests, or clinical interviewing. The first, self-reporting inventories, have reached a static level for pigeonholing individuals through factor analytic methods, but etiological bases for classification still elude us. Psychological performance tests have also reached (and perhaps passed) their zenith without providing us with useful classification. Clinical interviewing is the basis for psycho-pathological classification, and whether they can be useful for total human behavior I leave to you. Drugs, by actually entering the blood stream, provide an interaction with ongoing biochemical activity which may provide a much better classification system. The fact that there are such great individual differences in enzymatic activity as Dr. W. Kalow (1968) has pointed out should not trouble us. They may turn out to be largely quantitative, and individual dosage curves can yield the proper answer. There may however, be qualitative differences too—and these ought to be discoverable by biochemical means. Instead of brushing the ego lightly with questionnaires or titillating our sense modalities with light, sound, and touch, or evaluating behavior clinically, the injection of a drug under the skin which actually interacts with the biochemistry of the nervous system may give us a much better classification of human beings than we have now.

A recent syndrome, known as the Lesch-Nyhan Syndrome, has been noted in children that seems to be due to the complete absence of an enzyme (hypoxanthineguanine phosphoribosyl-transferase HG-PRTase). Such children exhibit compulsive, self-destructive and aggressive behavior, both physical and symbolic. The clinical syndrome is marked by mental retardation, neurological abnormalities (choreoathetosis or athetoid cerebral palsy), obsessive destructive behavior, and hyperuricemia. In the words of Byrne (1968), "It . . . appears to be the first condition to be recognized in which characteristic biochemical abnormalities are associated with a reproducible pattern of abnormal behavior."

With regard to the neurophysiological model, implanted electrodes in the brain may become no more rare than gold fillings in teeth, or pacemakers for hearts. Though implanted electrodes are still a rarity in humans, there have been reports of stimulation of certain portions of the brain that produce compelling pleasant and unpleasant sensations.

One of the characteristics of brain function is the screening mechanism which prevents overloading of sensory channels. Such stimulus barriers will be increased to prevent man from becoming overwhelmed by the additional hazards of noise, radiation, and weightlessness in space travel, and the circadian rhythm will be obviated. Currently latent new sense modalities may emerge in response to space flight.

The degree of uncertainty in a choice situation will be measurable by means of evoked potentials, and intentional and affective behavior will be directly observable through pupillographic measurement. Such specific measures of internal events can, of course, lead to interesting manipulations of behavior through drugs.

## SUMMARY AND CONCLUSIONS

I have listed some of the parameters of the etiological factors underlying each of the scientific models—ecological, developmental, learning, genetic, internal environmental, and neurophysiological. Some of the possible alterations of these parameters in the year 2,000 have been conjectured and possible choices offered. How will the new alignment of forces respond to drug effects? It is clear that with the alteration in the parameters, new needs may arise and demand satisfaction. I have elsewhere pointed out that no drug is an island unto itself working alone. Its physiological effects as well as its psychological or placebo effects interact with the entire pattern of innate and acquired behavior of the organism. Thus, adrenaline alone will not produce fear, nor will a fearful situation during which physiological feedback has been eliminated. It requires an interaction of the physiological and conceptual components to produce a fear response. For this reason, before drugs are proposed, a knowledge of the conceptual memory storage of the individual organism must be known and that is why, in the projection of the future, the addition of the new drugs must be studied against the background of the new sources of behavior operating in the year 2,000.

## REFERENCES

1. Anderson, S. (Ed.): *Planning for Diversity and Choice.* Cambridge: MIT Press, 1968. See also *Daedelus,* Summer 1967: *Toward the Year 2000—Work in Progress.*
2. Burdock, E. I.; Sutton, S., and Zubin, J.: Personality and psychopathology. *J Abnorm Psychol, 56*:18-30, 1958.
3. Byrne, W. L. (Reporter): Molecular approaches to the central nervous system. *Science, 162*:1416-1417, 1968.
4. Coppen, A.: The biochemistry of affective disorders. *Brit J Psychiat, 113*:1237-1264, 1967.
5. Dohrenwend, B. P., and Dohrenwend, Barbara S.: The problem of validity in field studies. *J Abnorm Psychol, 70*:52-69, 1965.
6. Hall, Marie B.: Robert Boyle. *Sci Amer, 217*:96-102, 1967.
7. Hamburg, David A., and Lunde, Donald T.: Relation of behavioral, genetic, and neuroendocrine factors to thyroid function. In Spuhler, J. N. (Ed.): *Genetic Diversity and Human Behavior.* Chicago, Aldine, 1967.
8. Hammer, Muriel, and Zubin, J.: Evolution, culture and psychopathology. *J Gen Psychol, 78*:151-164, 1968.
9. Harlow, H. F.: The heterosexual affectional system in monkeys. *Amer Psychol, 17*:1-9, 1962.
10. Hoch, P. H., and Zubin, J. (Eds.): *The Future of Psychiatry.* New York, Grune & Stratton, 1962.
11. Huisinga, J.: *Homo Ludens.* Boston, Beacon Press, 1950.
12. Jarvik, L. F., and Erlenmeyer-Kimling, L.: Survey of familial correlations in measured intellectual functions. In Zubin, J., and Jervis, G. (Eds.): *Psychopathology of Mental Development.* New York, Grune and Stratton, 1967, pp. 447-459.
13. Kalow, W.: Advances in pharmacogenetics. Paper delivered at the annual meeting of the American College of Neuropharmacology, December 19, 1965, San Juan, Puerto Rico.
14. Kanfer, F. H., and Saslow, G.: Behavioral analysis. *Arch Gen Psychiat, 12*:529-538, 1965.
15. Kreisman, Dolores: Social interaction and intimacy in preschizophrenic adolescence. In Zubin, J., and Freedman, A. M. (Eds.): *The Psychopathology of Adolescence.* New York, Grune and Stratton, 1970, pp. 299-318.
16. Papoušek, H.: Genetics and child development. In Spuhler, J. N.

(Ed.): *Genetic Diversity and Human Behavior*. Chicago, Aldine, 1968.

17. Salzinger, K.; Pisoni, S.; Feldman, R. S., and Bacon, P. M.: The effect of drugs on verbal behavior. Paper presented at symposium: Control of Verbal Behavior, American Association Advancement Science, Denver, Colorado, 1961.

18. Stern, Curt: Genes and people. *Perspectives in Biology and Medicine*, *10*:500-523, 1967.

19. Wolf, Richard: The measurement of environment. In *Invitational Conference on Testing Problems*, Educational Testing Service, 1965.

20. Zeaman, D., and House, B. J.: The role of attention in retardate discrimination learning. In Ellis, N. R. (Ed.): *Handbook in Mental Deficiency: Psychological Theory and Research*. New York, McGraw Hill, 1963, pp. 159-223.

21. Zubin, J.: A cross-cultural approach to psychopathology and its implications for diagnostic classification. In Eron, L. (Ed.): *The Classification of Behavior Disorders*. Chicago, Aldine, 1966.

# 2

## THE NEED FOR NEW INTOXICANTS
### MARTIN M. KATZ

THERE IS AN extensive philosophical and scientific literature which provides many ready explanations as to why man uses intoxicants. None of these explanations are completely satisfactory, so man continues to pursue and explore the bases for this pervasive and durable requirement of most cultures. We are aware also that, despite this inadequacy of understanding, if Western society determines that certain new types of drugs are needed, without question such agents can and will be developed.

Although it is true that scientists have not yet produced the "soma" that Aldous Huxley promised almost forty years ago in *Brave New World* (1932), it has to be admitted that they have created some remarkable approximations. It is likely that the major reason that the ideal drug has not yet appeared is more society's failure to be clear as to exactly what that drug should accomplish, what kind of state it should be capable of creating, than any technical inadequacies of the field of psychopharmacology.

Man's needs, it turns out, are neither unitary nor consistent; they vary in kind and in pattern across people, and within the same man, in relative strength from time to time. In view of this diversity of needs, the accomplishments in the field of drug development have been remarkable, i.e. in the variety of effects it is now possible to achieve through chemical agents. In fact, whether one thinks of the actions of drugs as merely effecting alterations of mood or whether their actions are interpreted in more profound terms, e.g. resulting in alterations of consciousness, transport of the self to another realm of consciousness, drug development has come a very long way in a relatively short period of time. We note that the span of effects man can attain with drugs extends from such relatively minor alterations as relief from tension to major changes in psychological states which include escape from lethargy, from boredom, from depression, through varying degrees of release from sexual and aggressive inhibitions and, ultimately, to complete transport of the ego to another reality. That is an impressive array of emotional states that one can escape from or to through chemical agents and ought to increase our confidence in attaining even more striking feats in the future.

To return to the uses to which intoxicants are put—I am not sure, despite the long history of attempts to explain their hold on the culture, whether their various roles in society have been thoroughly explored or described. There have been, over the years, some interesting descriptions of the psychological state that the intoxicant actually produces or accomplishes in man, what he actually obtains from the experience. It is important to consider whether the quality of man's needs for the state of intoxication will change in the future—or whether these needs will remain essentially the same and that we will simply have to continue to seek a truly reliable and more controllable intoxicant.

If we examine the statistics in regard to alcohol, the proportion of people who use it and the sheer quantity which is consumed, one might draw the conclusion that this culture has already found its "soma" and need not look any further. On the other hand, a great deal of alarming evidence has been accumulated about the psychological, social and physical effects of prolonged use of alcohol. The sequelae of excessive drinking, e.g. automobile accidents, family disruptions, and so forth, are serious and, again, well documented.* Some of these outcomes are not necessarily due directly to alcohol, but the reasons for them, like the omnipresent hangover, are tied as much to psychological forces within the culture as they are to the actual physical

---

* For a summary of current statistics and an otherwise comprehensive survey of the "alcohol problem" see Plaut (1967).

effects of the chemical agent.† Nevertheless, the physical effects of prolonged use are documented and the potentially destructive psychological effects, particularly following withdrawal after prolonged usage, are well known if not yet scientifically established. One of the more telling examples of the latter is A. E. Hotchener's description of the great author's demise in *Papa Hemingway* (1966). The chain of events in Hemingway's life which led to a kind of psychological deterioration was thought to be closely tied to the medical necessity to cease drinking abruptly, following some thirty years of a very heavy alcoholic regimen.

Given the wide range of problems with alcohol and the mild, so far reported, psychological and physical after effects of marihuana, some of its users have characterized the latter as possibly the ideal intoxicant for the American scene. There is relatively little hard evidence on the aftereffects of marihuana; only recently have investigators begun to pursue the type of laboratory research which may lead to answers concerning the effects of prolonged use (Isbell, 1967; Waskow, *et al.*, in press). Whether it is a desirable substitute is still an open question. Why we need intoxicants at all is a more interesting and provocative question.

Intoxicants, when used in relatively modest amounts, have the effect of altering the mood; in larger amounts they have the capacity for altering the state of consciousness, of possibly transporting the individual to an entirely different emotional or psychological state. This transport has been more graphically portrayed in descriptions of the reactions to the powerful psychedelic agents. Prior to the introduction of LSD, however, there were descriptions in the literature about the effects of alcohol and marihuana which were almost as vivid and as gripping. I will not, for the purposes of this discussion, try to distinguish between the psychological effects or overall impact of these agents—rather try to explicate what it is that they have in common. It is the capacity to "transport" the individual from one conscious state, from one reality, from oneself, to another

---

† If the culture did not, as has been suggested, have certain proscriptions against drinking, people might not have hangovers. In certain other cultures, e.g. Japan, in which there appears to be equally extensive use of alcohol, hangovers are relatively unknown.

psychological state which appears to be the common element in the effects of all of these drugs. Man has always appeared to have this requirement, but the reasons for it and the types of transport that are needed seem to change as a function of changes in the forces operating in the society in which he lives. If we accept some of the more profound explanations which have been provided in the philosophical literature concerning this need, then it can be viewed as part of the human condition likely to continue in strength regardless of changes in the outer world. It will be of value to review several of the more searching attempts to explain the basis for this need.

C. J. Jung (1923), for example, had a very complex theory about the dynamics of personality, about the conflicting forces operating within man and the internal battle for expression which is always in progress between certain facets of the personality. Man is inclined toward being a certain type of personality—either predominantly outwardly oriented, i.e. toward the world and external objects, or predominantly inwardly oriented, i.e. toward the self. Rather than see these as two completely discrete life-styles, this theory posits a continuing underlying inner conflict in the individual between these two basic tendencies. If one major type of personal expression dominates and therefore characterizes the individual's style of life, it is only because the other side is being suppressed by competing forces operating within the personality. The other side exists and is continually pressing for expression. It is only with certain major changes in the organism's physical or psychological state that the suppressed side finally manages some partial escape. According to Jung, aging is one of those processes which gradually upsets the balance of forces. A more rapid and more abrupt disrupter of this balance is alcohol. Alcohol creates a physical and psychological state which permits the release of the opposite facet of the personality; it permits the expression of the suppressed self. To the extent that the theory is valid, man is comprised of other selves and without the introduction of some intervening agent or process, physical or psychological, his awareness of, and the possibilities of expression of, these other selves is very limited.

We might agree that it is important to provide some assistance to the personality in achieving release of its other facets, that it is a good thing for expression of these hidden facets to occur— but some would undoubtedly argue that such abrupt disturbance of the integrity of the personality can have unfortunate consequences for the individual. Similar issues concerning its pitfalls arise when one considers William James' explanation for the attractions of intoxication. James, in that oft-quoted summary statement on the power of alcohol, remarked that whereas "sobriety diminishes, discriminates, and says no, drunkenness is, in fact, the great exciter of the *yes* function in man" (1902).

Although he saw its power as due mainly to its capacity to stimulate the mystical faculties of human nature, the statement could also be interpreted to mean that man under its influence is more open to the world about him, to invitations from the outside, more willing to subject himself to new and different experiences. Thus, the implication is there that certain kinds of perception of people and of the world are available to him that are not available in his more usual state, and that these other realities make him more fully aware of the potentialities of life. James was aware of the paradox here, one created by an agent which, on the one hand, he felt to be a poison, but which, on the other, he felt had within it the potential for producing a state which permitted a radical expansion of consciousness. The literary character who seems to best symbolize James' theory concerning the nature of this psychological state was the hero's young friend Dean in Jack Kerouac's *On The Road* (1957). Almost always under the influence of alcohol or drugs, his general response to life and everything that crossed his path was "yes" and Kerouac traces the wild, almost superhuman pace he maintained during his time-limited but unpredictable relationship with the novel's hero.

To cite a somewhat related and more contemporary explanation for the attractions of intoxication, we can look to Aldous Huxley's attempt to convey the meaning of the psychedelic experience and its relation to man's difficulties with the overwhelming domineering culture in which he develops (1954; 1964). To Huxley, the culture constructs an invisible fence around man; it weaves a network of traditional thinking-and-feeling patterns which become so much a part of his nature that he has difficulty distinguishing that perception of reality which is really his from that which is shaped and superimposed on his perception by the educational process of that culture. Intoxicants and psychedelic agents help to dissolve the cultural filters which dull the sensory apparatus, help to cut a hole in the cultural network so that man can see through the "given" reality to what he hopes is the true one.

Although the explanations so far presented seem to assume that man is unaware of these other selves or of other realities until exposed to an intoxicant or a psychedelic, I doubt that that is a completely accurate representation of the views of these thinkers. Chemical agents make it possible to more quickly validate the sense that man has that there is more to him than his own conscious awareness. Most theorists referred to, however, acknowledged the fact that there are other paths to these experiences; the alternative routes, it would be agreed, simply require more time to achieve what are the same goals. One of the reasons offered for the Americans' propensity for these agents is tied to this obsession with time and with efficiency. With these drugs there exists the hope, as Hayakawa has put it, of achieving instant relief of all spiritual ills, instant "satori," just as "we have *Rolaids* for instant relief of indigestion, and *Clairol* for instant youth and beauty" (1964).

There are two more familiar explanations for the powerful attraction of intoxicants which require consideration before attempting some sort of synthesis and prediction. General psychoanalytic theory speaks of their role in reducing inhibitions, particularly as regards sexual and aggressive drives. If no great harm comes from that release either to the ego or to outside objects of great significance to the person, then the behavior is reinforced and a kind of successful cathartic expression is thought to have been achieved. We note that instead of whole "selves" or "other realities" being referred to here, emphasis in this theory is on the temporary release of suppressed drives.

The most parsimonious of explanations, however, comes from a sociologist, Howard Becker (1963). In a discussion of the range of possible reasons which lie behind the use of marihuana, he proposes the hypothesis that there is nothing unusual or deviant about the motives which lead to its usage; it is rather its use which may lead to deviant behavior. He proposes that the individual usually comes upon marihuana as a fortuitous circumstance, may experiment with it simply out of curiosity, and then maintains the habit—only if he derives pleasure from it. His conclusion, then, might be that if someone learns to derive pleasure from marihuana, however he initially comes into contact with it, that more complex explanations are unnecessary; it is maintained simply because it is a new kind of pleasurable experience.

These are several explanations. We must consider now whether there is anything common among them, whether it will be necessary to provide an even more encompassing rationale for their use, and whether these explanations have something to tell us about our future relationships with intoxicants.

I would identify the primary emphasis in the Becker and in the psychoanalytic explanations to be on the sensual and the disinhibitory aspects of the experience; intoxicants afford pleasure or they afford a sort of relief through the cathartic expression of suppressed sexual and hostile urges while the individual is in a condition in which he need not feel responsible for the release.

The explanations of Jung, James and Huxley are more complicated. All seemed to speak of the release of other selves, of the experiencing of a different kind of reality, of both experiencing a new awareness of self and of the world around one. The impact that such experiences have on the future of the individual, on the stability of his personality structure and his perspective on the world are more profound; he may very well be changed in a more permanent sense as an outcome of the experience. There is that risk or that reward always attendant upon such encounters, especially upon those with the more powerful of the psychedelic agents.

Certainly the power of these agents to expand man's awareness of himself and the kinds of worlds in which he lives cannot in itself be a harmful force. After all we presume to seek the same ends through education, through travel, and through cultur-

ally broadening experiences. There must be something about
the suddenness with which these agents accomplish related ends
which is alarming, or the fact that most all of the chemical agents
are capable of also producing serious physical damage. Despite
the awareness of their potential for harm, large segments of our
population still experiment with these agents, i.e. alcohol, marihuana, LSD, a fact of life that must be communicating something
about the state of the culture, about its failure to provide very
satisfying alternative channels for the expression of the suppressed facets of personality.

There may well be, however, other very different motives
operating within individuals and within society which may be
equally powerful in encouraging the use of these agents. In
certain ways the intoxicants, through their capacity for disturbing
the internal balance of forces, can be viewed as agents which
promote disorder within the personality, as if the individual who
seeks them out may actually be seeking a mechanism for upsetting
the internal order. In this respect, then, I would propose, in
attempting to unravel the sources of their popularity and in
viewing the diverse roles of intoxicants in this society, that we
consider whether Western man may not have traveled too far in
his striving for control of his own life and of his future, in his
penchant for ordering his world and reducing the level of
unpredictability in nature. In suppressing all disorder within,
he suppresses the less organized and less coordinated facets of
his personality. In the course of attempting to control the more
disruptive emotions, he too often achieves a deadening of his
sensory life generally, and thus permits the cultural "filters"
which Huxley describes, to overwhelm his inner drives for reaching out and making contact with the real world. The power of
the intoxicants and the psychedelics to revive, in many cases,
the sensory apparatus reminds us that they may be only temporarily deadened and that under the right conditions the senses
can be reawakened. That these psychological states need not be
brought about solely through drugs is a lesson that artists like
the composer, John Cage, and the developers of the "Happenings"
have been trying to communicate for the past fifteen years.

I turn to the writings of the artist John Cage because his

is an extreme theory about human nature and the way to find real freedom of the spirit (1961; 1967). The theory, running directly counter to the emphasis on control and on order in Western culture, is based on the thesis that nature operates completely through chance, that life is essentially nonintentional, and that man's freedom lies in his giving his life completely over to chance. The expression of the theory is reflected in Cage's art; his music is composed in accord with this principle. If life and decisions are also left open to chance, the possibilities of new and different kinds of experiences in all spheres are always present. As an example, Cage initially used the "happening" to encourage the development of a receptive state in his audience in which all of the senses are subjected to some kind of intense and simultaneous stimulation. The aim was to nurture "polysensibility," i.e. a state in which several of the senses are in fact responding simultaneously, in which the individual permits the whole organism to respond, in which new psychological experiences are created. The giving over to chance in daily living also, in Cage's thinking, permits new things to happen, caters to the needs in human beings for new experiences and for expressions of otherwise dormant parts of their personality. The possibilities of discovering other selves and other realities in Jamesian terms are, therefore, greatly enhanced. This is, of course, a principle based on an extreme not easily put into practice, but it provides a useful counterpoint to the influence that Western science, mechanization, and man's need for control of his world and of himself has had on this culture.

Man's need to produce disorder in himself through psychedelics, his ever increasing need to produce disorder in his society, his need for greater awareness of the suppressed features of his own personality, his need to be in closer touch with reality, to have his senses reawakened, the existence of these drives provides some basis for investigating the many roles which drugs currently play in contemporary society.

If we wake up to these trends in time, our current array of intoxicants may in thirty years be superfluous. We may be able to accomplish all of these things without them. Man's need, however, to transport himself to another psychological state, to another if somewhat temporary reality, is not likely to abate a great deal between now and the year 2000. It would take a very radical change in the world and in him for that to happen. Our only recourse is to seek safer, more comfortable, and more satisfying ways for him to accomplish the same goal.

## REFERENCES

1. Becker, H.: *The Outsiders*. Toronto, Free Press of Glencoe, 1963.
2. Cage, J.: *Silence*. Middletown, Wesleyan University, 1961.
3. Cage, J.: *A Year From Monday*. Middletown, Wesleyan University, 1967.
4. Hayakawa, S. I.: Foreword: The quest for instant satori. *ETC.: A Review of General Semantics, 22*:389-392, 1964.
5. Hotchener, A. E.: *Papa Hemingway—A Personal Memoir*. New York, Random House, 1966.
6. Huxley, A.: *The Doors of Perception*. New York, Harper, 1954.
7. Huxley, A.: *Brave New World*. New York, Harper, 1932.
8. Huxley, A.: Culture and the individual. In Solomon, D. (Ed.): *LSD, The Consciousness-Expanding Drug*. New York, Putnam, 1964.
9. Isbell, H.; Gorodestzky, C. W.; Jasinski, D. J.; Claussen, U.; von Spulak, F., and Korte, F.: Effects of (-) $\triangle^9$-Trans-Tetrahydro-cannabinol in Man. *Psychopharmacologia, 11*:184-188, 1967.
10. James, W.: *Varieties of Religious Experience*. New York, Longmans, Green, 1902.
11. Jung, C. G.: *Psychological Types: Or the Psychology of Individuation* (Trans. by H. Godwin Baynes). New York, Harcourt Brace, 1923.
12. Kerouac, J.: *On the Road*. New York, Viking, 1957.
13. Plaut, T. F. A.: *Alcohol Problems: A Report to the Nation by the Cooperative Commission on the Study of Alcoholism*. New York, Oxford University Press, 1967.
14. Waskow, Irene; Olsson, J. E.; Salzman, C., and Katz, M. M.: Psychological effects of tetrahydrocannabinol. *Arch Gen Psychiat* (in press).

# 3

## CHEMICAL APHRODISIACS

WAYNE O. EVANS

### INTRODUCTION

THE SEARCH FOR chemical means to increase sexual appetite
and potency, and to maximize the sensual pleasures of sexual
relationships is as old as the recorded history of man. References to love potions to attract a desired partner or herbs
to renew a flagging sexual vigor can be found in the herbinals of
ancient Egypt and Greece.[1] By the time of the writing of Ovid's
"The Art of Love," a plethora of compounds had been suggested
ranging from mandrake to oysters.[2] Again, references to chemical
aphrodisiacs seem to know no cultural boundaries. Vedic poetry,
Chinese folk medicine, Melanesian legends, as well as western
history, all record man's search for these compounds. We can
say, with certainty, that this is a type of drug which normal
humans have always desired.

The desire to facilitate sexuality has been present in both
sexes, although references to chemicals for use with males seem
more prevalent. In examining a recent dictionary of aphrodisiacs,
compounds for male use outnumber those for female use by a
ratio of about fifteen to one.[3] This difference in motivation could
be due to woman's use of man's sexuality as a means of control,
the differences in ages at which women and men are most sexually
active or, possibly, the nature of a male's traditional self-image
as a virile, active hunter and fighter. However, for whatever
reason it occurs, the male of the species seems to desire relatively
more dearly a chemical means to support his sexual activities.

As one examines literature from different cultures across the
years, certain common beliefs about chemical aphrodisiacs can

35

be noted. First, fish, vegetable products from the ocean, such as seaweed, and phosphorus itself have been presumed to restore a flagging potency in males.[4] This belief has been held in China, ancient Greece, Europe and, to some extent, is still with us in modern western society. Similarly, truffles have a long and geographically varied history as aids to male potency.[5] The cubeb pepper and various aromatic spices also have been believed by many to act as a sexual stimulants to both sexes.[5] One must wonder if some truth may exist in these beliefs when they come from such widely dispersed sources. Certainly, these older beliefs do offer some interesting possibilities as starting points for a modern drug development program. Recently, a compound composed of nux vomica, yohimbine and methyltestosterone has been placed on the market as an aid to sexual appetite and capability for the impotent.[6]

Of late, the enhancement of sexual sensuality, as opposed to the facilitation of potency, has come into prominence. This property has been attributed to a wide variety of chemicals. In eastern countries, canabis products are used by a substantial number of people to add luster to the sexual experience.[7] Similarly, LSD has been used in this country as an aid to the esthetic aspects of sexual relationships.[8] Also, opiates are believed by their users to contribute to the capacity of the male to prolong erection and, thereby, lengthen the sexual act.[9] Amyl nitrite recently has been used to enhance sexual pleasure.[10] All in all, it is obvious that mankind always has wanted, and still wants, to enjoy more frequent and more exciting sexual relationships.

## II.  POTENTIAL APPROACHES TO DEVELOPING CHEMICAL APHRODISIACS

Sensual sexuality is not a simple phenomenon governed by only one aspect of physiology. Therefore, a single chemical should not be expected to fulfill all of the desired requirements. In order to consider aphrodisia, we must separate its various aspects and then look for different chemicals which will affect these diverse elements.

Traditionally, the reduction of interpersonal inhibitions by intoxicants has been regarded as leading to an enhancement of the desire for sexual relations. Even in times of history in which sexual inhibitions were not strongly enforced by the society, e.g. Imperial Rome, intoxicant consumption still accompanied orgiastic activities.[11] Also, during the present era, we find alcohol consumption prominently associated with sexual crimes.[12] Similarly, some husbands and wives take LSD or canabis derivatives together to accompany sexual activity.[13] It would seem that barriers to intimate interpersonal relationships exist even in situations in which social sanctions are not involved. Intoxicants act to reduce the effectiveness of these inhibitions and, thereby, release the sexual appetite.

Stimulant chemicals have been reported to increase the sensual enjoyment of sexual activities. Leary has proclaimed in a *Playboy* interview that "LSD is the most powerful aphrodisiac known to man." From India, Chopra reports the use of canabis for this purpose.[7] "Speed," i.e. desoxyephedrine, cocaine and other chemicals which act as adrenergic activators have also been indicated as intensifying the sexual experience. Even caffeine at very high doses reportedly has this effect. A recent report demonstrates that in rodents, the excitement produced by an electric shock increases sexual responsiveness.[14] A general state of CNS excitement would appear to be conducive to the promulgation of an intense sexual experience.*

Opiates, although depressant in most of their actions, seem to increase the duration of male capabilities. This has been reported for regular heroin users.[9] This activity may be related to the parasympathetic activation associated with the use of these chemicals and the resulting stimulation of the peripheral mechanisms of sexual activity.[15] On the other hand, it could result from a depression of the ejaculatory reflex without a concomitant depression of erectile capability. Opiates, however, do not seem to contribute to either sexual appetite or enjoyment. It would be interesting to observe the effects of an opiate-like drug with little depressant activity, such as cyclazocine[16] or methadone,

---

* Since the original manuscript was prepared, L-dihydroxyphenylalanine and para-chlorophenylalanine, both adrenergic drugs, have been implicated as aphrodisiacs (see Addendum).

or a parasympathetic stimulant, such as pilocarpine mixed with an adrenergically activating intoxicant, to see if the increased capability could be combined with enhanced pleasure and reduced inhibitions.

In certain people, both tranquilizers and antidepressive substances have improved sexual performance. These drugs seem particularly useful in cases of premature ejaculation or with sexually anxious people. Their effects, probably, mainly are due to an amelioration of mild mental illness, however, and therefore could not be considered as true aphrodisiacs for normal humans.

Long-term aspects of sexual desire and performance in both males and females are largely dependent on a minimum level of androgenic hormones.[17] Testosterone can increase the sexual responsivity in females of a number of species, including humans.[18] Also, adrenalectomy in the female often leads to diminished responsiveness, whereas ovariectomy does not.[19] In the male, castration or lowered testosterone titers due to aging may result in a diminished desire and capability for sexual activities.[20] These androgenic substances do not seem to be necessary for sexuality, but a minimum level appears to be highly facilitory to it.

From these considerations of the effects of different chemicals, it would appear that sexual appetite, capability and enjoyment are governed by different physiological and psychological systems. Further, sexual appetite seems devisable into the reduction of inhibitions, a general state of activation, as well as a specific motivation. Capability may refer to the duration of the activity, its frequency or recovery rate. Enjoyment of sexuality appears to separate into a reduction of inhibitions, enhancement of sensation and a general, stimulated euphoria. To expect a single chemical to optimize all of these functions, simultaneously, is highly improbable. However, a mixture of chemicals would seem a possible means of accomplishing this condition.

### III.  CONTROL OF THE SEXUAL ACT

The sexual act has been shown to be controlled by a combination of genetic, neonatal, chemical, neural, psychological and sociological factors. Of these, the psychological and sociological seem to be the prepotent variables. Castrated animals with previous sexual experience continue to be capable of the sexual act,[21] and genetic females with phenotypic male characteristics can still perform the sexual act.[21] Yet, a monkey deprived of a tactile "surrogate mother" or an opportunity for peer social relationships when young cannot engage adequately in sexual behavior,[22] and variations in the location of high schools can totally change the frequency and attitudes toward sex by the students.[23] Again, the nature and the novelty of the sexual partner is as important to the sexual responsiveness of rodents[24] as it is to man,[3] and for proof of the necessity of an appropriate social role image for sexual behavior, one need only study the history of the institution of marriage.

Genetic factors seem to exhibit their predominant effect by controlling the hormonal milieu of the fetus and neonate.[25] The sexual behavior of either a male or female can be reversed if the preponderance of one type of hormone over another is reversed during the fetal period in humans or during the neonatal period in rodents.[21]

Hormones exert an effect upon sexuality all during life, but not as a direct "trigger" for the sexual act. As was previously mentioned, a minimum level of androgenic hormones is facilitory to sexual responsiveness in both sexes. That androgens normally do not serve as a "trigger" to the sexual act is demonstrated by the continuation of some sexual performance after the decline in androgens due to age or castration. The amount of remaining sexuality seems primarily dependent on the amount of previous sexual experience by the animal or human.[21] On the other hand, direct placement of testosterone in the preoptic area of the brain can induce immediate sexual activity in rodents.[26, 27]

Irritant and chelating chemicals introduced directly into the lower brain can elicit motivated, as opposed to reflexive, sexual behavior within seconds after administration.[27] Sites in the hypothalamus and preoptic area have both been shown to be able to exhibit this effect. Thus, target areas do exist in the CNS which can directly and quickly instigate sexual behavior. Direct stimulation of the hypothalamus by electrical current also can elicit motivated sexual behavior within seconds after onset.[28, 29, 30, 31,] Similarly, it has been shown that lesions of paleocortical brain tissue can either generally help or hinder sexual behavior.[32, 33, 34]

The interpretation of these findings of the existence of localized brain areas which "trigger" sexual behavior must be that the instigation of the sexual act is at least partially controlled by the limbic brain and Papez cycle. Further we must conclude that sexual behavior is a discrete response, subject to control by chemical or electrical intervention. Thus, a specific chemical instigation of sexual appetite seems possible in the same sense in which other chemicals have been found to directly affect the chemoreceptor trigger zone for nausea or in which drugs affect medullary respiratory control.

## IV. TECHNIQUES FOR MEASURING SEXUALITY

In order to search for chemicals which can affect the various aspects of sexuality, we must have measurement methods in a variety of species to establish "screening" procedures. Further, the measurement methods for animals must be shown to have predictive validity to man.

Adequate techniques of measurement of latency of sexual approach, frequency of copulation, number of intromissions, number of emissions and recovery time have been developed for use with lower mammals. Beach[33] and others have shown reliability of these methods and used them to study neural and chemical controls of sexual activity. These measurement procedures have shown the similarity of man and lower mammals in their dependence on androgens and in the importance of the limbic brain in sexuality.[20] Thus, some degree of predictive validity has already been demonstrated for these methods, and, therefore, they can serve as the basis of a drug screening program.

In nonhuman primates, one may observe all the same responses found in lower mammals and, additionally, the blatency of sexual display, dominance relationships and amount of noncoital sexual behavior.[34] That these observations are relatable to human sexual responsiveness can be shown by noting that the same types of factors, i.e. maternal relationship, novelty of mate and appropriateness of the environment, are important in both monkey and man. These methods also may serve as part of a screening program.

Finally, man himself can be studied by means of questionnaires, physiological responsiveness to manipulation, attitudes and behaviors toward sexual partners, etc. These measures will provide the criterion variables for the screening procedures used in lower mammals and other primates and for the final clinical tests of compounds which are developed. Kinsey,[35] Masters and Johnson[36] and others have shown both the reliability and feasibility of these methods.

We then may conclude that the measurement of sexual activity in man and animals has been studied to an adequate degree to make the development of a screening procedure to test chemicals for their effects on the various aspects of sexuality eminently feasible. We are far better prepared for measurement in this field than we previously were to measure pain, tranquility or other types of psychotropic drug action.

## V.  IMPLICATIONS OF THE DISCOVERY OF APHRODISIAC CHEMICALS

The American culture has been described by Herman Kahn as moving toward a "sensate society.[38] By this term, he means that a greater emphasis is being placed on sensory experience and less upon rational or work-oriented philosophies. Within such a culture, aphrodisiac chemicals would be accepted and contribute to a general view of sexual behavior as a desired, pleasurable sensory experience. Such a philosophic view, coupled with the means to separate sexual behavior from reproduction or disease, will undoubtedly enhance sexual freedom.

We also can anticipate an outcry and vigorous attacks against the marketing of aphrodisiacs from certain groups. To combine the presumed evils inherent in the words "drug" and "sex" in one product would be just too provocative to overlook. However, the fascinating field-day offered to advertising companies by chemical aphrodisiacs should overcome the indignation of the few. The present use of the term "sex appeal" to describe a toothpaste and the prevalence of sexual attractiveness references in all of the mass media demonstrate that the precedent has already been set.

To conclude, mankind has always desired aphrodisiacs. It would seem that we now have appropriate screening methods and some hints on the type of chemicals to examine. It will probably be only a matter of time until chemical aphrodisiacs are with us and in widespread use. Let us hope that society can integrate the use of such chemicals into its institutions so that they can be a source of additional strength to our society rather than a cause of dissension. The use of such chemicals can as easily lower divorce rates as it can increase promiscuity. The choice as to the result of their use lies in the hands of those people who shape our social evolution as "role models." What middle-aged people, such as you and I, think or want to believe has little importance in these developments. As we consider the effects of these advances in pharmacology we must ask: (a) to whom do the youth listen? (b) what are their social and personal values? (c) in what kind of a world will young people live? It seems to me to be obvious that the youth of today are no longer afraid of either drugs or sex. Again, the philosophers and spokesmen for the avant-garde advocate the personal sensory experience as the raison d'etre of the coming generation. Finally, we are moving into an age in which meaningful work will be possible only for a minority. In such an age, chemical aphrodisiacs may be accepted as a commonplace means to occupy one's time. It will be interesting to see if the public morality of the next thirty years will change as much as it has in the last thirty.

If we accept the position that human mood, motivation, and emotion are reflections of a neurochemical state of the brain, then drugs can provide a simple, rapid, expedient means to produce any desired neurochemical state that we wish. The sooner that we cease to confuse scientific and moral statements about drug use, the sooner we can rationally consider the types of neuro-chemical states that we wish to be able to provide for people. The old argument of the "morality of naturalness" in the production of moods, motivations or emotions seems somewhat of a lost cause in our present, almost totally artificial, environment. We may expect, that in the year 2000, to make judgments based on the "morality of naturalness" will be even less meaningful than today. Therefore, I submit to you, that if we wished, we could probably have an effective set of chemical aphrodisiacs within a period of as little as five years.

## REFERENCES

1. Licht, H.: *Sexual Life in Ancient Greece.* London, Routledge, 1932.
2. Thompson, C. J. S.: *The Mystic Mandrake.* London, Rider, 1934.
3. Wedeck, H. E.: *Dictionary of Aphrodisiacs.* New York, Philosophical Library, 1961.
4. Davenport, J.: *Aphrodisiacs and Love Stimulants.* New York, Stuart, 1966.
5. Heartman, C. F.: *Cuisine de l'Amour.* New Orleans, Gourmet, 1942.
6. Margolis, R.; Sangree, H.; Prieto, P.; Stein, L., and Chinn, S.: Clinical studies of the use of Afrodex in the treatment of impotence: Statistical summary of 4000 cases. *Curr Ther Res,* 213-219, 9, 1967.
7. Chopra, I. C., and Chopra, R. N.: The use of cannabis drugs in India. *Bull Narcotics, 9 (No. 1):* 1957.
8. Barron, F.: Motivational patterns in LSD usage. In Debold, R. C., and Leaf, R. C. (Eds.): *LSD, Man and Society.* Middletown, Conn., Wesleyan University Press, 1967.
9. Fiddle, S.: *Portraits From a Shooting Gallery.* New York, Harper and Row, 1967.
10. Linken, A.: In Sengton, D.: *Psychosocial Aspects of Drug Taking.* London, Pargamon, 1965.
11. Kiefer, O.: *Sexual Life in Ancient Rome.* London, Routledge, 1934.
12. Gebhard, P. H.; Gagnon, J. H.; Pomeroy, W. B., and Christenson, C. U.: *Sex Offenders.* New York, Harper and Row, 1965.
13. Blum, R., *et al.: Utopiates: The Use and Users of LSD.* London, Tavistock, 1965.
14. Barfield, R. J., and Sachs, B. D.: Sexual behavior: Stimulation by painful electric shock to skin in male rats. *Science, 161:*392-393, 1968.
15. MacLean, P. D.: Studies on the cerebral representation of certain basic sexual functions. In Gorski, R. A., and Whelan, R. E. (Eds.): *Brain and Behavior.* Los Angeles, University of California Press, 1966, vol. III.
16. Jaffe, J. H.: Psychopharmacology and opiate dependence. In Efron, D. H. (Ed.): *Psychopharmacology: A Review of Progress, 1957-1967.* Government Printing Office, 1968.
17. Money, J.: Sex hormones and other variables in human eroticism. In

Young, W. C. (Ed.): *Sex and Internal Secretions,* 3rd ed., Baltimore, Williams and Wilkins, 1961, vol. II.

18. Waxenberg, S. E.: Some biological correlates of sexual behavior. In Winokur, G. (Ed.): *Determinants of Human Sexual Behavior.* Springfield, Thomas, 1962.

19. Waxenburg, S. E.; Drellich, M. G., and Sutherland, A. M.: The role of hormones in human behavior. I. Changes in female sexuality after adrenalectomy. *J. Clin Endocr, 19:*193-202, 1959.

20. Ford, C. S., and Beach, F. A.: *Patterns of Sexual Behavior.* New York, Harper & Hoeber, 1951.

21. Sawyer, C. H.: Reproductive behavior. In Field, J. (Ed.): *Handbook of Physiology.* Baltimore, Williams & Wilkins, 1960, vol. II, section 1, Neurophysiology.

22. Young, W. C.: Genetic and psychological determinants of sexual behavior patterns. In Hoagland, H. (Ed.): *Hormones, Brain Function and Behavior,* New York, Academic Press, 1957.

23. Reiss, J. L.: Sociological studies of sexual standards. In Winokur, G. (Ed.): *Determinants of Human Sexual Behavior.* Springfield, Thomas, 1962.

24. Fowler, H., and Whalen, R. E.: Variations in incentive stimulus and sexual behavior in the male rat. *J Comp Physiol Psychol, 54:*68-77, 1961.

25. Hart, B. L.: Neonatal castration: Influence on neural organization of sexual reflexes in male rats. *Science, 160:*1135-1136, 1968.

26. Fisher, A. E.: Maternal and sexual behavior induced by intracranial chemical stimulation. *Science, 124:*228-229, 1956.

27. Fisher, A. E.: Behavior as a function of certain neurochemical events. In *Current Trends in Psychological Theory.* Pittsburgh, University of Pittsburgh Press, 1961.

28. Vaughan, E., and Fisher, A. E.: Male sexual behavior induced by intracranial electrical stimulation. *Science, 137:*758-760, 1962.

29. Lisk, R. D.: Inhibitory centers in sexual behavior in the male rat. *Science, 152:*669-670, 1966.

30. Caggiula, A. R., and Hoebel, B. G.: "Copulation-reward site" in the posterior hypothalamus. *Science, 153:*1284-1285, 1966.

31. Meyers, R.: Evidence of a locus of the neural mechanism for libido and penile potency in the septo-fornico-hypothalamic region of the human brain. *Trans Amer Neurol Ass, 86:*81-85, 1961.

32. Klüver, H., and Bucy, P. C.: Preliminary analysis of functions of the temporal lobes in monkeys. *Arch Neurol Psychiat (Chicago), 42:*979-1000, 1939.

33. Kling, A.: Effects of amygdalectomy and testosterone on sexual behavior

of male juvenile macaques. *J Comp Physiol Psychol, 65*:466-471, 1968.

34. Harris, G. W., and Levine, S.: Sexual differentiation of the brain and its experimental control. *J Physiol, 163*:42-43P, 1962.

35. Beach, F. A.: A review of physiological and psychological studies of sexual behavior in mammals. *Psychol Rev, 27*:240-387, 1947.

36. Mirsky, A.: The influence of sex hormones on social behavior in monkeys. *J Comp Physiol Psychol,* :327-335, 1955.

37. Masters, W. H., and Johnson, V. E.: *Human Sexual Response.* Boston, Little, Brown, 1966.

38. Kinsey, A. C.; Pomeroy, W. B., and Martin, C. E.: *Sexual Behavior in the Human Male.* Philadelphia, Saunders, 1948.

39. Kahn, H., and Wiener, A. J.: The next thirty-three years: A framework for speculation. *Daedalus,* Summer 1967.

## ADDENDUM

Levo-3, 4-dihydroxy-phenylalanine (L-DOPA) is the centrally active precursor of dopamine which, in turn, can be converted into norepinephrine; the probable neurohumor responsible for central sympathetic activity. L-DOPA presently is being used as a chemotherapeutic agent for Parkinson's disease, a disorder characterized by severe tremor during intentional movements. A side effect found in about 2 percent of patients receiving L-DOPA is an increased sexual drive coupled with antisocial behavior.[1, 2] This, again, may indicate that adrenergic stimulation facilitates sexual responsiveness.

Para-chlorophenylalanine (PCPA) acts to inhibit the formation in the brain of 5-hydroxytryptamine (serotonin). Thus, it reduces the amount of a chemical which tends to antagonize central sympathetic stimulation in a number of functions. Increases in sexual responsiveness have been reported for rats, rabbits, cats and, some evidence suggests, it also may occur in humans of both sexes.[3, 4]

The effects of these adrenergic stimulators in facilitating sexuality probably is due to a lowered threshold for sexual responses, i.e. less acceptable partners would elicit the sexual act more often than normally would be the case.[5]

## REFERENCES

1. Cotzias, G. C.; Papavasiliou, P. S., and Gellene, R.: Modification of parkinsonism-chronic treatment with L-DOPA. *New Eng J Med,* *280*:337-   , 1969.

2. Barbeau, A.: L-DOPA therapy in Parkinson's disease: A critical review of nine years experience. *Canad Med Ass J., 101*:59-   , 1969.

3. Tagliamonte, A.; Tagliamonte, P.; Gessa, G. L., and Brodie, B. B.: Compulsive sexual activity induced by p-chlorophenylalanine in normal and pinealectomized male rats. *Science, 166*:1433-1435, 1969.

4. Ferguson, J.; Henriksen, S.; Cohen, H.; Mitchell, G.; Barchas, J., and Dement, W.: "Hypersexuality" and behavioral changes in cats caused by administration of p-chlorophenylalanine. *Science, 168*:499-501, 1970.

5. Whalen, R. E., and Luttge, W. G.: P-chlorophenylalanine methyl ester: An aphrodisiac? *Science, 169*:1000-1001, 1970.

# 4

## DISCUSSION

### W. J. TURNER

To DISCUSS AND COMMENT on specific aspects of the preceeding papers would be a formidable task. Instead, let me attempt to put them in a larger perspective. To do this I must get away from the here and now, planning for a city in 1975, and from the Community Health Programs anticipated for the future. None of these plans make sense except in the context of what we are as human beings, how we got here and what we are doing now. On the basis of a retrospective summary, we can perhaps more clearly anticipate something of the future.

I had planned to spend some time on the subject of our vertebrate phylogeny which began some 600,000,000 years ago and must already have been well developed when the first Placoderms invaded fresh water. At that time already there was the part of the nervous system developed which would permit anticipation of the future. This was in the form of the distance receptor associated with chemical sensations in the primitive olfactory mucosa. As Papez has so excellently described, the olfactory tract ended in a tripartite division. The lateral division entering the forebrain, associated with what became the lateral forebrain bundle, has bequeathed to us our aversive responses, negative feelings, disgust, fear and anger. The medial division came in contact with those structures which have given rise to the medial forebrain bundle and its derivatives to which we owe our pleasurable anticipation, our appetite and our curiosity. This pleasurable anticipation is not the same as gratification in consummatory action. The intermediate division, which receives impulses both from the lateral and medial divisions, became the primitive motor organizer for functions of avoidance or approach.

Martin Katz and Wayne Evans discussed phenomena arising out of a relative balance of excitation in the forebrain bundle structures, excitations which give rise to that eternal human search for some profound ultimate gratification. It is this which has led people to have religious ecstasies and to search for Nirvana. The more we are uncertain in the time of need for decision, the greater the excitation in this system which, now coupled with eyes and ears, we use for analyzing and anticipating the possible survival in and gratification from the future.

With respect to the city planning for 1975, another aspect of our vertebrate evolution comes to mind. This has to do with population problems. Some years ago John Calhoun and his associates undertook extensive and intensive studies of the ecology of the Norway rat. Under crowded conditions these animals develop a range of behavior which is definitely abnormal when contrasted with behavior of animals in open field. For example, in one set of experiments he set up several rooms measuring 10 x 14 feet, dividing them into four sections by partitions. In each section there were towers which led to nesting boxes. On the floor there was always plenty of food, plenty of water, and plenty of nesting material. Five pairs of rats were placed in each room. Shortly, the great majority of the animals were found to congregate in one of the compartments, giving rise to what Calhoun called a behavioral sink. In this sink, the population density increased with perhaps eighty out of one hundred animals in one compartment. The consequences of this behavioral sink were extreme. Descriptions of some of the animals are very strongly reminiscent of our own human psychopathology. Calhoun pointed out that the rats had come to their present way of being over millions of years of development with their genetic constitution in balance with their environment. Suddenly, within the space of a few generations, they were faced with an entirely new kind of environment. It is in this rapid change of environment, and particularly in the constraints of the captivity in the behavioral sink that pathology develops.

Sir Charles Darwin wrote a book some years ago which he called *The Next Million Years*. In it he claimed that the human being is the only wild animal without a master and with no one to master him. I claim that human beings are wild animals in captivity. As such we have to look not to the animal in its natural state but to what it is in captivity. I think it is not helpful to shrug off these observations as being ratamorphism. The same kind of phenomenon has been found in chimpanzees in an artificially created behavioral sink.[1] In these chimpanzees there are other facets than the hierarchy of dominance and submission. Some animals remain completely indifferent to the existence of other animals. There are the isolates, the sexual and maternal failures, in short, animals vastly different in their behavior from those described by Jane Goodall.

Let us remind ourselves that these phenomena occur as population density increases and as our cities get larger and larger. While we may be planning all sorts of social programs, drug programs, and economic innovations, our biological tendencies to congregate into denser and denser communities will negate every effort that mankind can make to better his state. A strong argument can be advanced that, while population control does not assure us that any human problem can be resolved, we may be confident that no human problem can be solved until there is population control. The city of the year 2000 may be nonexistent.

Let me note another aspect of the relationship of our present world to our past. Students of evolution have long been aware that every new form of life has taken off from the old by modifying a structure and a function present in the use of the ancestral form. In a sense, life is getting forever younger. It was old at its beginning. Mankind is an eternal adolescent derived from a species which was probably playfully aggressive in its youth. One of the marks of human adolescence is the violent extremes to which it is prone: to asceticism on one hand and to licentiousness on the other. These tendencies in man have given rise to the extremes of the orphic and the stoic philosophies.

History has innumerable examples of waves of aggression and rebellion and violence alternating with troughs of quiescence, submissiveness and order. We are all familiar with the ambivalence of the rebellious students of today, but this is no new thing under the sun. What is different today is the enormous number of healthy youths throughout the world, healthy as a consequence of improved medication and improved nutrition. Right now it is easy to prophesize doom, but we might be reminded that these rebellious youth grow up and in the next twenty years they will be the parents, the Babbits, the Establishment. We may expect that at that time the sexual revolution which we see now is going to be strongly suppressed.

To summarize, there are four major areas with which psychopharmacology will deal. Namely, sex, aggression, pleasure and unpleasure.

With regard to sex, we can inhibit it as the Puritans did and as I suppose our children will be doing twenty years from now. With the increase in population density, we can expect a great deal of homosexuality and of forms of sublimation. It is conceivable that there will be attempts to use drugs, either pre- or immediately postnatally, for the prevention of sexual activity. For instance, cyproterone injected into women at some early phase of pregnancy may result in testicular feminization of the males. These persons will grow and develop as females, a clinical phenomenon now well known. Postnatally, it is possible that this drug will permit a male to develop, but without sperm. The possibility of producing large numbers of sterile human beings will involve many questions of ethics and economics. Aside from the production of sterile human beings, the use of drugs in children may so markedly alter their behavior that they will become unhuman adults. What, for instance, if there were radioactive drugs which would localize in a specific area of the limbic lobe? Naturally, as Wayne Evans has suggested, there will be drugs self-sought for their capacity to enhance the sense of sexual delight. These will be those which yield not anticipations but gratification. The neurophysiology of gratification is still to be learned.

Now, as to aggression, we can anticipate an increase in the number of drugs which are used by physicians or by authorities to diminish aggression, and at the same time there will be an increasing number of drugs, which we call tranquilizers, which will be sought by those who wish to use it on themselves. As Joseph Zubin has said, some of the drugs which are now used, such as alcohol, diminish the sense of interpersonal distance and even permit contact, otherwise impossible. Some of these drugs, such as the ones now socially used, can become further sanctioned by authority and even surreptitiously promoted. There is in this field another potential use for radioactive compounds which would localize specifically within the limbic lobe, particularly in areas connected with the lateral forebrain bundle. Perhaps these would first be introduced as therapeutic agents.

Now, as to pleasure, which of course is intimately tied up with sex, with exploration, with curiosity and with hope. All of these are related to the functions of the medial forebrain bundle but may also be inhibitors of lateral forebrain bundle functions. If rabies is a virus which more or less specifically irritates the lateral forebrain bundle structures, is there a virus which would impair it without excitation, or which would produce bias in the medial forebrain bundle?

With regard to unpleasure, pain, fear, disgust, hunger, with the situation of famine already present in this world and expected to increase enormously, there will probably be drugs such as cocaine which will diminish the pain of hunger. These may be home-grown. While tranquilizers now tend to produce an indifference to pain and to fear, more active agents in this regard are certain to be sought and be used. We already have many psychological mechanisms for turning off a response to another person's cry for help. We look at violence on television. We remain indifferent to overt sexual abberations. Insofar as drugs can be used to render human beings indifferent to suffering of themselves or others, they will be used.

Before closing, there are only two more comments to make, dealing with life-long modifications of behavior. One is that along with the drugs of avoidance, which I have been discussing, there will continue to be treatments for improvement, even sometimes a search for ways to promote the best of humanity and the best of creativity. Among these, there may be more extensive attempts to alter genetic constitution. These attempts will first probably be made in the field of disease, such as in the Hurler and Hunter syndromes, in which mucopolysaccharides are excreted. In each of these syndromes, there is a metabolic incompetence, but when cells from persons afflicted with each of these diseases are grown in tissue culture and combined, or combined with normal cells, something takes place which causes an interaction, such that thereafter all cell lines become competent and normal. The treatment of genetically determined diseases, some of which give rise to such extreme aggression or pain, may be treated by giving a child metabolically adequate cells. Again, the moral, economic and genetic consequences of such actions must be carefully considered.

Now, as a final note, José Delgado has given some beautiful illustrations of what can be done with implanted electrodes in human beings. There is another way coming up, that is, by use of a tiny capsule of silicone, permeable to drugs in which very minute amount of drug can be encased. This can be placed in a specific location in the central nervous system, such that the drug can leak out, molecule by molecule, over long periods of time to modify activity in and only in its immediate vicinity. If such drugs and implants can be adapted to the individual body chemistry they will permit control of aggression, excessive fear, hypersexuality and other behavior, perhaps for the effective lifetime of the individual.

## REFERENCE

1.  Kollar, E. J.; Edgerton, R. B., and Beckwith, W. C.: Evaluation of the behavior of the ARL colony chimpanzees. *Arch Gen Psychiat*, 19:580, Nov. 1968.

---

*Editor's note*: Dr. Delgado recently presented a paper titled "Permanent Appeasement of the Monkey by Micro-Injections of Chemicals into the Brain."

# 5

## SPECULATIONS ON THE USE OF PSYCHOTROPIC DRUGS IN GERONTOLOGICAL PRACTICE IN THE YEAR 2000

### HEINZ E. LEHMANN

**D**r. Lehmann: Gerontology is the science which deals with the processes of normal aging, and I shall discuss the possible uses of drugs to improve performance in aged people who are otherwise healthy—and let my imagination roam into the future.

It is estimated that the United States population in the year 2000 will be about 310 million. Thirty million will be over sixty-five years of age and twenty million will be over seventy-five.[1] The possible life span of the people at age seventy-five will probably not have increased substantially in the year 2000, because until now there has been no real increase in the biological life span. But there has, of course, been a tremendous increase in actual life expectancy because more people can now live until their biological clock runs out, which has always been around seventy-five. Very few people in the year 2000 will be over eighty-five, but there will be many more people aged seventy-five and eighty in the year 2000 than there are today.

What is aging? According to one definition, aging is the increased probability of death. In fact, the probability of death increases as a function of age, and somebody who is thirty-five has a much lower probability of dying—about twenty per thousand will die at that age—than he has at the age of eighty, when about 130 per thousand will die, and after that the probability goes up even more steeply.[2]

The constantly increasing probability of death is, naturally,

53

anxiety producing—it must evoke in every normal human being some sort of apprehension of annihilation—an apprehension that one may call "existential anxiety" or anguish.

Let me briefly review the present theories of aging. We know very little about normal aging since its scientific exploration is only just beginning.

## CURRENT THEORIES OF AGING

There are at present three main theories of aging. One is the *exhaustion and accumulation theory.* The second is the theory of *molecular changes,* and the third is the so-called *error theory.*[3]

The exhaustion-accumulation theory is based on the fact that certain substances in the organism become exhausted as time passes. We all know this. For instance, the aging gonads produce less and less testosterone and female sex hormones. And ovulation will stop because there is only a limited number of ova in the ovary, and when the supply is exhausted, well—there isn't anymore. With the exhaustion theory goes the accumulation theory. It is a chemical theory postulating that there is an accumulation of "klinker" substances, for instance lipofuscin, which increases 0.6 percent per year in the heart muscle. In the heart muscle and in the brain the constant accumulation of lipofuscin is most observable. It is a useless age pigment which simply chokes up the cells.

The second theory of aging, the molecular change theory, assumes—and actually has some experimental evidence to prove it—that molecules which originally are properly formed in the organism change with time, mainly through the effects of radiation. Cosmic rays penetrate every cell in the body and there are also other radiation hazards: exposure in nuclear industry, exposure to medical x-rays, nuclear device fall-out etc. Ionizing radiation can change molecules. What happens then in the organism, for instance in connective tissue, is that cross-linkages in collagen take place. As an example, it can be shown very simply that a rat's tail will stiffen with age. We observe similar phenomena in the skin, in bones, in blood vessels, i.e. these cross linkages within collagen molecules of an aging organism.

Finally, the third theory of aging, the error theory assumes that the nuclear DNA changes, which means that the information mechanism in each cell begins to convey to other cells erroneous information on protein formation; it thus serves as a false template. In fact, since the DNA molecule is extremely stable, it is assumed that it is not DNA itself which is changed but the messenger RNA whose role it is to take messages from the DNA to the cells where protein is formed in the ribosomes. The messenger RNA is probably being deformed by radiation. Mutations due to RNA or DNA-induced chromosome changes as a consequence of radiation have been well studied, and it seems that aging is to a considerable extent caused by radiation.

To these three current theories of aging one might add a fourth recent hypothesis which explains the physical changes occurring with age by autoimmune processes involving antibodies to an individual's own organs. These antibodies are thought to increase with age, leading to gradual self-destruction of the organism from within.[4]

## ANTIOXIDANTS AND FREE-RADICAL SCAVENGERS TO PREVENT AGING

In a recent paper, Tappel, a nutritionist at the University of California, has proposed some interesting theories on the prevention of aging.[5] He thinks that by giving antioxidants one might prevent or, at least slow down, the molecular changes in the cells. He points out that when one studies radiation damage chemically one finds that it is mainly due to peroxidation, more specifically peroxidation changes due to polyunsaturated lipids. Now, polyunsaturated lipids are the substances we are told to increase in our diets in order to prevent atherosclerosis. We are, for instance, told to eat margarine because there are more polyunsaturated lipids in it than in butter. The American diet contains about 40 percent lipids, and 70 percent of these are polyunsaturated. Many people try to increase this proportion in order to prevent atherosclerosis but, at the same time, they also increase the risk of cellular damage due to peroxidation, the result of ionizing radiation in polyunsaturated lipids. Peroxidation forms free radicals. Free radicals are dangerous because they are molecules with free electrons which have a lot of energy, race around and damage cell membranes, damage lysosomes—the organelles in the cell—and free hydrolytic enzymes. This causes general chaos in the cell which cannot completely digest all parts of its injured membrane. Thus the cells choke up with parts of undigested, damaged membrane.

It can be shown in different ways that the age pigment lipofuscin is, in fact, a product of the lysosomes which have not been able to do their job completely. Lysosomes stain for acid phosphatase and so does lipofuscin; both lysosomes and lipofuscin fluoresce yellow because they contain flavants, and the electron microscope will actually show parts of undigested damaged cell membrane in lipofuscin. This leaves little doubt that lipofuscin really is an "age pigment" resulting from cellular damage—in other words, the klinker of cells injured due to radiation.

What can we do about it? We cannot walk around in lead armor to protect ourselves from radiation. Since free radicals do the damage in the cells, substances are needed that trap these free radicals and make them innocuous. Tappel suggests that antioxidants could serve as free-radical scavengers. There are three possible ways to do this. Vitamin E is a natural scavenger, according to Tappel (apparently animal nutritionists know a good deal more about this than human nutritionists). There are also water soluble free-radicals scavengers, e.g. ascorbic acid, vitamin C, which has definitely synergistic effects with Vitamin E.

Finally there are radiation protectors, e.g. cysteine, glutathione, and sulfhydril proteins. We know that sulfhydril proteins, to some extent, are effective radiation protectors. This has been shown in animal experiments where aging has actually been retarded by giving these sulfhydril proteins. Therefore, Tappel concludes that we should increase our vitamin E and vitamin C intake, i.e. both the lipid-soluble and the water-soluble scavengers of free-radicals, and as radiation protectors take more sulfhydril proteins, cysteine, glutathione and similar substances, yet to be discovered.

I am sure this is something on which the nutritionists will

soon go to work energetically, and it is conceivable that by the year 2000 we will have quite effective drugs which will minimize radiation damage and will take care of preventing the accumulation of waste products in the cells—the lipofuscin, for instance.

Now, let me go on with a little fantasying about new and less orthodox possibilities in addition to these more or less scientifically based things.

## THE UNIVERSAL DEFECTS OF AGING

First, I would like to review the universal defects and disabilities of aging. By universal I do not mean features which depend on whether somebody ages in India or in the United States, but those features which refer to common factors, remaining largely invariant under different cultural and other environmental conditions. Muscular weakness develops as one gets older. This is possibly due to accumulation of lipofuscin, because lipofuscin accumulates mainly in muscle and brain. Because of muscular weakness there develops increasing slowness and impairment of general mobility.

Another general disability in old age is impairment of memory in all its phases, i.e. perception, storage and retrieval—again possibly associated with the fact that the brain is one organ system where lipofuscin develops.

There is also impairment of new learning in old age, which is not the same as memory impairment. It is related to the latter, but somebody might conceivably have a good memory for simply storing and retrieving material and still not be able to assimilate and integrate new concepts. We know that "an old dog doesn't learn new tricks."

These are some universal disabilities of old age. I mentioned already that the cerebral impairment is possibly due to lipofuscin and general aging of colloids, because we find senile plaques in the aging brain. In senile dementia there are a tremendous number of them. Senile plaques are probably just aged colloid which "has gone sour" and precipitated—one of the molecular changes of colloidal substances.

## SUBSTITUTION OF HORMONES AND RNA

We need better methods of substitution therapy. We know that testosterone and female sex hormones can be used successfully in fighting the disabilities resulting from the deficiency of these substances, but there are still many undesirable side effects to this treatment. For instance, in one study we gave fifty geriatric patients testosterone, but had to discontinue the treatment of two because their transaminase increased to pathological levels; in others, there was a definite trend towards an increase. Liver function impairment with testosterone is still too frequently encountered. There also remains some doubt about the carcinogenicity of these hormones.

What about the lipofuscin that has accumulated? Is it not possible that we might find something (like an exchange resin?) which would actually clear those choked up cells of lipofuscin and get it out of the system?

And, possibly, we might develop something like a polyvalent RNA. I say polyvalent, because if we theorize that our messenger RNA is damaged and therefore our memory impaired, we would need replacement RNA—RNA that serves not only rats or rabbits or yeast cells, but also man. Cameron has done a great deal of work on RNA injections for aged people with memory impairment and has claimed that their memory improves when he injects RNA obtained from rats or yeast.[6] He did not know which RNA was the most suitable. His results have never been confirmed by others. However, messenger RNA is probably a highly individual substance, just like DNA. It is difficult to conceive that one may take any yeast RNA and hope that it will bring the right messages to human brain cells. A substance is needed which has certain general characteristics that may help memory storage, possibly by aiding protein formation in brain cells.

## SOCIO-PSYCHOLOGICAL HAZARDS

So much about the biological aspects of future drug uses in the aged. What about the social and psychological hazards of aging? Again, I want to concentrate on the common denominators, the invariant universals in culture. Threats and deprivation I would see as the main psychological hazards.

Threat—financial worry—is probably facing old people everywhere, although perhaps not yet so much in the Eastern cultures where the aged are kept in the family which respects them and provides for them. But even in the Eastern cultures, it will probably soon be a realistic worry for older people that they might run into financial difficulties. In the United States, right now, things do not look very encouraging. During the last two or three years, there has been a 4.5 to 5 percent inflation every year, and with the present trends the old age pension will not keep pace with the increasing inflation, so that in twenty or thirty years from now people with old age pensions might be way behind the galloping inflation and possibly suffering from poverty.

Of course, the senior population has voting power, but only about 10 percent of the population is over sixty-five years of age. Even in the year 2000, politicians will not listen much to this small vote, no matter how poor old people might be by then, unless, of course, the politicians in the year 2000 will be more responsible than they are today. And since many politicians of the year 2000 will be the people who are activist students today, they might well have a keener social consciousness than our politicians of today.

An interesting experiment has recently been reported. In the Medical School of a California University a questionnaire was prepared to test the prejudices of the students directed against the aged. When these students were asked whom they would save of two drowning persons—a Negro and a White—50 percent refused to answer. But when the question was changed to an old person and a young person, only 5 percent refused to answer and 95 percent replied that they would save the young one. However, when I asked one of our East Indian psychiatric residents, who is now working for his MSc, about the probable findings of this kind of questionnaire in India he said, "Oh, our thinking is quite different there. Indians would have saved either a very young child or the very old person, not the young adult in the middle."

True, there are cultural differences in the attitude towards the aged, and in some cultures the aged are not rejected as they are in our Western technocracy. But increased anxiety of the older person is really a universal reaction which is not only culturally determined. It is anxiety about illness, about death, about loneliness, because these are the "existential givens" of any aged person. He is much more susceptible to illness, much closer to death than the younger, and he always will be; he is also very lonely, because many of his friends have died and he will never again be quite as popular as when he was younger.

And the aged suffer deprivations: social deprivation because of loneliness, sensory deprivation because their senses become dulled. One old lady said, "A pickle doesn't taste like a pickle anymore." Sexual gratification is not what it used to be. The appreciation of visual beauty is attenuated, if not muted. Few old persons are still capable of expressing enthusiasm, rapture and enchantment, and many lose the sense of their own value because they have become less capable and thus less valuable for society.

## THE DISENGAGEMENT THEORY

Let me refer briefly to another theory, i.e. the Cummings' theory of aging which one may call the disengagement theory.[7] According to the authors of that theory, the aging person—or even the middle-aged person—begins to disengage himself more and more from society as society disengages itself even more from the older person. The authors distinguish between two types of people, the impingers and the selectors. Impingers are those who affirm and confirm their self-concept by constantly trying it out in interaction with other people. On the other hand, a selector's life style is characterized by waiting for the right cue coming from the environment to confirm his self-concept. These types age in different ways. The impingers, constantly depending on social interaction, are gradually becoming handicapped. Their judgment is slipping; they are slowing down. They might become a little confused, because they have to interact and they can no longer cope as well. The selectors, on the other hand, waiting for the right cues—which may never come—run the danger of becoming inert and apathetic as they get older and less involved and as society progressively disengages itself from them. Thus, in the disengagement process the impingers are threatened by confusion and anxiety and the selectors by apathy.

## SPECULATIONS ON FILLING THE REAL NEEDS

Now, having said all this, let me briefly comment on what is constantly being preached today in papers and editorials in geriatric journals, in talks by learned physicians etc., whenever they try to come to grips with the problem of human aging. In the end it always develops that we have to teach through psychotherapy, through example, rapport and persuasion, that the young have to show respect for the old, that they have to honor them, and that in return the young might expect the older to exhibit resignation and a dignified acceptance of their fate.

But an old person needs love just like any younger person—not respect. Respect does not satisfy his instinctual need. What can he do with respect? Difficult as it may be to provide love for him, he can, at least, be made to *feel needed*. Feeling needed is probably the best substitute for love—a better one than just being respected. This is a social issue, of course. But as physicians we will have to find ways to prepare older people to do jobs where they are really needed.

Instead of honors, receiving one honorable mention after another which they may put on the walls of their room, old persons need a *feeling of achievement*. How to bring this about is another social and psychological problem. We will have to find positions for senior people, and roles where they are needed and can find achievement.

But perhaps we should, in addition, find drugs that would at least give them a fantasy or an artificial sense of achievement. The sense of achievement, i.e. the gut feeling "I have done something quite well," is an experience which can probably be induced by pharmacological means. For instance, a person who has done a day of skiing often feels that he has done a great thing—just as though he had finished a full day of important work. Yet, all he has done is ten miles of cross-country skiing or fifteen times up and down the ski-tow hill. If somehow he gets this peculiar feeling of achievement through such an irrelevant stimulus as having performed some physical exercise, this experience must have a physical substrate in the CNS, which, eventually, we might learn to trigger off with a drug.

What old people need is not resignation and dignity but pleasure, as we all do. We will have to find drugs that will make it possible for them to get a keener appreciation of the beauty around them—and make a pickle taste like a pickle again.

There are already drugs of this kind, for instance, sodium glutamate; this substance if added to seafood or other dishes enhances their taste. It would seem to me that such substances should be a regular dietary addition to any old persons' food. We should not wait until people begin to complain that their senses are becoming dull. Rather, from the beginning of these physiological changes, i.e. at age sixty or so, taste enhancing substances should be added regularly to the food of aging people, before they become depressed because they realize that for the last five years life has not been what it was before, even if only because their taste for food has changed.

*Mental slowness* and *mental rigidity* are partly—probably to considerable part—due to accumulated lipofuscin and changed brain chemistry. But I have a theory of my own, that a great deal of this mental slowness, and also the memory loss of old age, are functional and due to the fact that people's minds have become jaded. The longer we live, the more we have seen. Finally we get to the point: "Well, I have seen it all. I have seen the Carribean and Europe. I have been everywhere. I have heard all operas. I have tasted all the food there is." Nothing is new anymore and we develop what psychologists would call anterograde or satiation inhibition; we do not register or store any novel sensations and do not react intensely anymore because we are too filled with old memories.

Therefore, what will have to be done is to produce some sort of "cleaning of the blackboard," to produce once more a temporary feeling of newness in the aged person and wipe away the feeling that everything is forever familiar and unexciting. Perhaps someday, somebody will even have the courage to give electroconvulsive therapy (ECT) to a person who is getting old but has remained well preserved except for a complaint of *early memory loss.* It would take quite a lot of courage because, as is well known, the ECT procedure by itself produces temporary memory impairment. Yet the disinhibiting effect of ECT might well outweigh its amnesia-producing effect. A temporary radical amnesia might have a salutary effect on the aging person suffering from insidious, slight memory loss. If then exposed to all kinds of entirely new experiences for a few weeks, he might regain his zest for living because he regained the exciting feeling of unfamiliarity of his youth and with it perhaps some of his old enthusiasm. It is conceivable that, freed from old ballast, his memory will even improve, because he might again begin to register and store impressions and he might also begin to concentrate on new experiences and overcome the functional, inhibitory disabilities of rigidity, slowness and functional memory loss.

I mentioned already the possibility of combating memory loss with RNA. There are other promising drugs in the fight against memory loss, e.g. nicotinic acid and testosterone which we have tested experimentally with some favorable results.[8] And there are probably many more metabolic and hormonal agents which have the potential of improving memory.

Experimental psychologists have shown repeatedly that cholinergic drugs seem to be involved in the learning of avoidance conditioning. (Strychnine seems to have similar effects.)[9, 10] Such findings from animal experiments may eventually be applied to people, and cholinergic drugs may become a therapeutic factor in improving the *learning of new experiences.*

Sedatives and neuroleptics are available for the control of *emotional instability* of aged people. The important thing is not to induce drowsiness in the old person. Thus, we need tranquilizers which produce greater emotional stability without inducing drowsiness at any dose level.

Then, there is what we may call the *depressive bias* of the old person. As I mentioned before, it is the existential consequence of having lived a long time. The old person has experienced many losses and he feels a lingering hopelessness, because—what is there to look forward to? The future holds a great deal less, instead of a great deal more as it would for any younger person.

This means that we need antidepressants for old people, but not just any antidepressants. The drugs we need ought to be specifically focused on anesthetizing a person to the sense of loss and the constant *ruminations* over it. The normal mourning process over losses in the young or middle-aged individual serves an important purpose and is self-limited, because younger people eventually become attached to new things. But for the libido of the older person, there is not very much new to which it might attach itself; therefore, the results are often hopelessness and never-ending ruminations.

Thus, what we need is a drug which will reduce these ruminations over losses or anesthetize a person to his sense of loss, just as we can anesthetize him—with anxiolytic sedatives—to the sense of threat.

*Guilt* in the old person is not much of a problem. In the younger person we need antidepressants that can reduce guilt feelings, but in the older person that is not really so important.

*Anxiety* is most troubling for the impingers—those elderly whose life style compels them to interact constantly. Because they are no longer fully confident of their ability, they become anxious and feel threatened. Their existential and social anxiety leads to withdrawal, hoarding and defensive inhibition. Medications here should consist of drugs from the class of anxiolytic sedatives.

These drugs produce increased conflict behavior in animals and also in humans.[11] This means that if there is a conflict of wanting something and, at the same time, wanting to avoid it—for instance, food for a rat given simultaneously with electric shock—then the anxiolytic sedative will decrease the value of the aversive (punishment) stimulus and enhance the value of the positive (reward) stimulus. That is precisely what we need for older pepole. They should experience a greater appreciation of the positive things in life and a diminished perception of its negative aspects. Drugs to induce such experiences exist already, because most anxiolytic sedatives possess this property of altering the experience balance in favor of the positive aspects of a situation—a property which is not always an unmixed blessing and may have dangerous consequences (e.g. addiction) in a younger person, but would be a desirable feature for an aging person.

We also need *disinhibiting* drugs for the elderly so that they may, under controlled conditions, regress; but we need something better than alcohol, something that does not produce a hangover and liver cirrhosis. In other words we need a better alcohol, a shorter acting one, which would allow an aged person for an hour or two to get "drunk," if he wants to, and then recover promptly. The potential of marihuana for this purpose should be seriously considered.

Further, we need something to abolish the *sleep disorders* of the elderly, particularly the kind of early morning insomnia which the Germans call "senile Bettflucht," meaning the senile flight from bed. Many old people wake up around four or five in the morning and have to get going then because they become anxious. But they do not really know what to do, and everybody else in the house resents their restlessness at that hour.

Thus we need hypnotics which will prevent them from having to get up so early, drugs which will be effective mainly in the early hours of the morning. We also need drugs that will control the quality of sleep, not just its quantity since it is now well established that old people are deficient in the phases of deep sleep (state IV).

We also need drugs that will allow us to modify the nature of *dreaming*. Old people who lead an anxious life and have to face many hazards frequently have bad dreams and nightmares. There seems to be no reason why someday we might not find a drug which will influence the nature of our dreams, produce serene and pleasing dreams instead of threatening ones. Why could we not eventually learn to steer the brain pharmacologically towards favoring dream mechanisms and contents which are acceptable and euphoric rather than horrible and nightmarish?

And finally, older persons should probably take every day a mild analgesic, because various *aches and pains* become very frequent as life goes on, being biological consequences of aging. Yet, these troubling symptoms of aging can quickly and effectively be eliminated with ordinary, mild analgesics.

To sum it up then, the Public Health nurse—not necessarily

the doctor—of the year 2000 should see to it that an old person
who lives alone gets large amounts of vitamins—megadoses of
vitamins, i.e. thousands of milligrams of ascorbic acid and perhaps a thousand milligrams of niacin a day. I think this will be
the trend. The elderly should also get—with their morning coffee
—a mild analgesic every day. It does not have to be much more
than aspirin. Old people should get a hypnotic every night—
not just to put them to sleep, but mainly to be sure that they
do not wake up too early in the morning. All this could be
routinely administered by members of the family or by a Public
Health nurse. Also routine would be a mild antidepressant to
desensitize the old person against the constant, existential feeling
of loss, and a mild anxiolytic or a stimulant, depending on whether
the person is an impinger—in which case he should be given an
anxiolytic—or a selector, in which case he should have a stimulant.

These, then, would be drugs that should be given every day.
But I also have a fantasy of a strategy for special problems of
some old people.

Since an old person is beset by so many hazards and liabilities
and since he has become socially disengaged but at the same
time needs greater involvement with and greater acceptance by
society—why not have an old person sleep under drugs three to
five days a week? During this time he could be easily supervised
by a Public Health nurse or by his relatives who would just go
and feed him small amounts of food at regular intervals. Then,
for one or two days of the week, the old person will be allowed
to wake up, and this awakening will be timed in such a way that
some special and pleasant events will take place on that day.
It will be the one or two days when the old person works, or
will go to a party or the opera or the circus or on a short trip, or
whatever it is. On these days, he will also be given a special
stimulant—perhaps a mild hallucinogen—which will enhance his
experiences and will keep him extraordinarily alert.

This would also mean that on these particular days he will
perform like a much younger person, and therefore will be more
appreciated by those younger people who are with him. On
those days, for a few hours, he will perform as though he were
in his forties. He can do this because of the stimulant he received

and also because for the last three or five days he has been saving energy while he was hibernating and not exposed to the wear and tear of having to ruminate about his worries, his boredom, his loneliness. During the limited times he is awake for one or two days a week, he is indeed aware and intensely "with it."

*Dr. Evans*: Thinking of Eric Kass' work on the anticipation of death, your description of the lack of appreciation and the need to enhance sensation and the feeling of loneliness makes me think of Danny Friedman's description of LSD as a "cultogenic" drug. It would seem to be that in a sense you are describing a whole series of phenomena for which we now have a good drug—LSD under carefully controlled conditions of administration.

*Dr. Lehmann*: Yes, I think that should be thought of on the days when there is nobody visiting, nobody to take them out for a drive, nothing to do. On such bleak days, if they are not asleep, there might be an LSD experience, perhaps in a group—controlled situation—at any rate, something to look forward to, because to have nothing to look forward to is the most terrible thing for an older person—or for any person.

*Dr. Gorsi*: Concerning the universal aging phenomena, I think it is important to try to relate the human experience in physiological aging to that of the animals. Now, why is it that the Virginia red deer or the California mountain lion, which have approximately the same body weight as the human being don't show the same aging rate? Why is it that radiation seems to affect them so much more than it does humans? What is the mechanism by which human beings resist aging as magnificently as they do?

*Dr. Lehmann*: I suppose it is evolution, i.e. natural selection, that is responsible for the slower aging of the human species. We seem to have a tougher messenger RNA than the deer and the mountain lion.

## REFERENCES

1. The future aged: New requirements and new expectations. *Geriatrics* (Geriscope), 23:18, 1968.

2. Jones, H. B.: A special consideration of the aging process, disease, and life expectancy. In Lawrence, J. H., and Tobias, C. A. (Eds.): *Advances in Biological and Medical Physics.* New York, Academic Press, 1956, vol. 4.

3. Shock, N. W.: Biologic concepts of aging. In Simon, A., and Epstein, L. J. (Eds.): *Aging in Modern Society* (Psychiatric Research Reports of the American Psychiatric Association. Washington, February, 1968.

4. Walford, R. L.: The role of autoimmune phenomena in the aging process. *Sympos Soc Exp Biol, 21*:351, 1967.

5. Tappel, A. L.: Will antioxidant nutrients slow aging processes? *Geriatrics, 23*:97, 1968.

6. Cameron, D.; Sved, S.; Solyom, L.; Wainrib, B., and Barik, H.: Effects of ribonucleic acid on memory defect in the aged. *Amer J Psychiat, 120*:320, 1963.

7. Cumming, E.: New thoughts on the theory of disengagement. *Int. J. Psychiat.,* 6:53, 1968.

8. Lehmann, H. E., and Ban, T. A.: Pharmacological load tests as predictors of pharmacotherapeutic response in geriatric patients. Presented at the Seventh Annual Meeting of the American College of Neuropsychopharmacology, December, 1968, San Juan, Puerto Rico.

9. Brimblecombe, R.: Effects of centrally acting drugs on acquisition of a passive avoidance reaction in the rat. In Bente, D., and Bradley, P. (Eds.): *Proceedings of the Fourth Meeting of the Collegium Internationale Neuropsychopharmcologicum,* Elsevier, Amsterdam, 1964.

10. McGaugh, J.; Thomson, C.; Westbrook, W., and Hudspeth, W.: A further study of learning facilitation with strychnine sulphate. *Psychopharmacologia, 3*:352, 1962.

11. Lehmann, H. E.: Tranquilizers: Clinical insufficiencies and needs. In press in *Excerpta Medica* Foundation.

# 6

## MANIPULATION OF LIFE PATTERNS WITH DRUGS

NATHAN S. KLINE

> A drug is a chemical substance which,
> when brought into contact with a living
> organism, produces a paper.

T RADITIONALLY DRUGS HAVE been used for the rapid relief of dangerous or painful pathology. After a few thousand years the physician finds it difficult to regard this situation as anything but "normal," and the use of pharmaceuticals for purposes other than such treatment usually strikes him as improper.

Fortunately for the preservation of hundreds of millions of individuals through the centuries, the disease and its pragmatically derived treatment coincided sufficiently in most cases to have made it possible to function in general ignorance of a substantial number of other relevant factors,* such as mode of action. Only now that we are struggling slowly out of a protoscientific stage have we begun to progress beyond such glorified first aid. Without the existence of electron microscopes, mass spectrometers, computer hardware and radioisotopes, our capacity for investigation was limited. Thus medicine was traditionally in large part an art, and there are some who resist changing this condition.

It is not, however, equipment and techniques but conceptualizations which are really most basic to change. In attempting to analyze how drugs alter life patterns we are forced into unusual

---

* In the long run, of course, the physician may contribute substantially to the undoing of the human race by perpetuating, popularizing and reinforcing a defective genetic mass.

considerations. The material is familiar but the way it has to be considered is new. This shift in the frame of reference requires a reformulation which has broad relevance. In itemizing how life pattern alteration may occur as a result of drug use we begin with that which is best known to us (see Table 6-I).

TABLE 6-I

WAYS IN WHICH DRUGS CAN ALTER LIFE PATTERNS

1. Correction of Existing Symptoms
2. Correction of Potential Pathology
3. Prevention of Acute Symptoms
4. Prevention or Relief of Chronic Symptoms
5. Acute Drug-induced Pathology
6. Pathology Induced by Chronic Drug Use
7. Minor Reality-relievers
8. Induction of Transcendental States

## I. WAYS IN WHICH DRUGS CAN ALTER LIFE PATTERNS

### A. *Correction of Existing Symptoms*

There are a surprisingly large number of persons who suffer from diseases which affect their life style. High on such a list would be chronic depression which may manifest itself in such forms as fatigue, underachievement, hypochondriasis, etc., as well as in its more obvious manifestations. Appropriate treatment can alter the total life pattern. As one patient put it, "Now for the first time I feel like I always knew I should feel."

Not only relief of abnormal psychological states (anxiety, phobias and obsessions, etc.) but also pharmacological treatment of physical pathology (hypothyroidism, diabetes, chronic prostatis, colitis, etc.) can entail a radical alteration of life pattern.

### B. *Correction of Potential Pathology*

The administration of drugs may prevent the development of conditions which would be severely disabling by supplying some missing ingredient as in pellagra, cretinism and other endocrine deficiency disorders, etc. A curious reversal is phenylketonuria where the treatment is to subtract from the diet as far as possible the amount of phenylalanine since it cannot be appropriately metabolized. There are several similar amino acid and other inborn errors of metabolism whose correction radically alters the way the life pattern will develop.

### C. Prevention of Acute Symptoms

Excruciating pain, uncontrolled euphoria, dementia and deliria can abruptly precipitate irreversible changes. Thus prevention of such acute symptoms by anesthetics, tranquilizers, etc., may similarly alter a life pattern by preventing its disruption.

### D. Prevention or Relief of Chronic Symptoms

Recurrent or continuing pathology such as angina, mucous colitis, hiccoughs, or depression can lead to profound alterations in how one feels, thinks and acts. Thus drugs which prevent or relieve such states are profoundly life-altering. Current interest in lithium (for recurrent affective disorders) is one example of the importance of this approach.

### E. Acute Drug-induced Pathology

At times alterations in life patterns can be produced by deliberate or accidental use of drugs on a single occasion. One of my most notable failures in treatment was a Ph.D. in psychology studying with Anna Freud in London who attempted suicide with cyanide. The resultant impairment was an immovable and inseparable mixture of physical and psychological trauma which in no way damaged his intelligence but nevertheless made him hopelessly and retrogressively dependent.

In susceptible individuals, LSD and similarly acting drugs may produce permanent dissociation after a single administration.

### F. Pathology Induced by Chronic Drug Use

The character of the Mad Hatter in Alice in Wonderland was drawn from life. In the preparation of felt for hats, mercury was commonly used and the fumes plus the quantity accidentally ingested produced a type of organic deterioration resulting eventually in dementia. Thus a sizeable number of hatters did become "mad" as a result of chronic mercury poisoning.

It may well be that chronic air pollution, chemical sprays

of food or radioactive fall-out may someday be found to have had a similar effect on our own life patterns.

### G. Minor Reality-relievers

Drugs are widely used to alter life patterns in ways other than the correction or production of gross pathology. In our own culture there are tens of millions of persons whose lives are markedly more happy because of the use of caffeine, alcohol, nicotine and even amphetamines and barbiturates. Unfortunately with some of these drugs (e.g. alcohol, amphetamines, barbiturates) a percentage of users become abusers. In other instances (e.g. nicotine) there may be unfortunate side effects such as heart disease and cancer. In others (e.g. coffee and tea) there are only very rarely undesirable consequences. There is some reason to be hopeful that methods of preventing addiction can be developed. This will be discussed subsequently.

In different cultures other drugs have been used for similar purposes, e.g. cannabis sativa (whether as hashish, bhang, marihuana or some other form), qat (kat), coca leaves, etc.

Controlled use in one culture by no means guarantees that a drug can be imported "safely" into another culture. The introduction of alcohol to the American Indian or of opium to India and China had disastrous consequences. It is too early to tell what results cannabis use will have here.

### H. Induction of Transcendental States

The recorded use of drugs in conjunction with religious or mystical ecstasy dates back at least as far as the Eleusinian Mysteries and probably even earlier to the time of the Egyptian middle kingdom. The actual beginnings are lost in protohistory. From hashish use by the "hashashin" (assassins) under Hasan Sabah to the hallucinogenic candles burned at the witches' Sabbaths to current use of LSD to induce "psychedelic" states there has always been a great value placed on drugs to effect major conversions of life patterns. Drugs may produce dissociation and perceptual pathology (including hallucinations), but obviously a great deal more is involved in determining what will result. This brings us to the next section.

## II.  FACTORS DETERMINING HOW DRUGS INDUCE ALTERATIONS OF LIFE PATTERNS

Aside from the chemical structure of the drug itself and its "expected" action on the organism there are other influences which determine what actually does happen (see Table 6-II).

TABLE 6-II

FACTORS DETERMINING HOW DRUGS INDUCE
ALTERATIONS OF LIFE PATTERNS

1. Hereditary Potentials
2. Environmental Conditions
3. Psychological Structure
4. Expectations
5. Physiological State
6. Timing

### A.  *Hereditary Potentials*

There was until fairly recent years a great neglect of pharmacogenetic influence. It has now been clearly demonstrated that certain drugs act quite differently in different genetic strains. The impetus to a good deal of this work was the demonstration in 1938 that atropine esterase occurred in some rabbits but not others. This explained the puzzling observation (made in 1852) of Schroff, a Viennese physician, that some strains of rabbits enjoyed eating belladonna leaves that were fatal to other rabbits. In 1959 McClearn and Rodgers[1] demonstrated "clear and pronounced strain differences in alcohol preference of highly inbred groups." The possibility of the preference being due to learned behavior was ruled out since "Pups cross-fostered on mothers of other strains showed preference patterns consistent with the genetic rather than the foster line."

Certain strains of mice will even drink to their own detriment.

We thus conclude that we have demonstrated a close analogue to the condition of human alcoholism: specifically identifiable physiological changes of an undesirable sort, resulting from prolonged voluntary ingestion of alcohol by animals with alternating access to adequate diet, continued their level of ingestion following the physiological changes.

In a study of ninety children whose mothers received antenatal progesterone, Dalton[2] found that of those given progesterone as compared with matched controls:

1. more were breast-fed at six months.
2. more were standing and walking at one year.
3. more received significantly better grades in academic subjects, verbal reasoning, English, arithmetic, craftwork, but did not differ in physical education from the controls. The very best results were found when more than 8 grams of progesterone was given prior to the 16th week of pregnancy.

Even more specifically, prenatal gonadal hormones differentiated masculine and feminine patterns of mating behavior as well as several other forms of behavior. The behavioral differentiation is attributed to an organizing action of androgen on the portions of the brain in the central nervous system which are destined to mediate sexual behavior.

Briefly, it is known that when androgen is present in the fetus, the genital tract of genotypic males and genotypic females is masculinized; when androgen is absent, genital tract development tends to be of the female type. Dr. Young has observed analogous effects on behavior; when androgen is present in the fetus, genotypic males and females display masculinized behavior, attributed to masculinization of the central nervous system. When androgens are absent, genotypic males and females display feminine behavior, attributed to feminization of the central nervous system. Feminization is attributed to an *absence* of androgen and not to the presence of estrogen.

The implications of this work are, of course, very great. Dr. Young suggests that at birth the organism is bisexual and that sexuality is then differentiated. I wonder if it wouldn't be more correct, in view of the profound differentiating and organizing effects of androgen, to view the organism as basically feminine and then differentiate it by androgen. . . . The question, of course, arises whether other endocrines—e.g. thyroid and other chemicals—applied in the fetal or in the antenatal period can similarly produce durable behavioral alterations. For the psychiatrists the implications for psychosexual development, both normal and pathologically distorted, are highly important. Hopefully, new possibilities will be open for understanding the genesis of hemosexuality and psychosexual aberrations.[3]

## Dr. Young[4] himself writes

We[5] presented the results (that) gonadal hormones secreted prenatally act on the developing mammalian brain in such a way that the predominant pattern of behavior displayed during the juvenile period and after the attainment of adulthood is masculine or feminine.

The effect of testosterone administration altered not only sexual behavior, but response to other medications. There appears to be a period during which the brain is maximally susceptible to the action of prenatal gonadal hormones. In the guinea pig this lies between the twenty-fifth and thirty-fifth day of gestation.

In other work it has been shown that the length of the phallus, the frequency of mounting, intromission and ejaculation are all related to prenatal hormone administration. A large variety of traits are related to early administration of androgen and feminine traits determined by the absence of early steroid hormones. The range includes the social behavior of rhesus monkeys, cyclic running behavior and emotional response in rats, metabolic rates in oxygen consumption in guinea pigs and micturitional behavior patterns in dogs.

Similarly, the capacity of drugs to alter life patterns in one individual but not in another in many cases may be related to similar hereditary potentials.

## B.   Environmental Conditions

Physical environment has long been known to influence drug response. The amount of oxygen available (high or low altitude), season and the temperature of the environment are obvious factors.

Certain drugs such as barbiturates and alcohol are "disinhibitors" and resultant behavior depends strongly on the social environment. If given to an individual in a quiet room they usually induce sleep, but if given to the individual who is attending a noisy party there is usually overstimulation.

At times hereditary factors interplay with environmental

circumstances. Stimulants such as the amphetamines are about eight times as toxic to mice crowded into one large cage as to litter mates caged singly. However, for certain strains of mice (DBA/2 or BDF mice) this susceptibility does not hold. Thus social environmental conditions as well as physical ones can be shown to influence drug response in animals as well as in humans.

## C. Psychological Structure

Di Mascio et al.[6-16] have shown that anxiety-prone individuals respond in a different way to medication than do those not so inclined. Introversion and extroversion tendencies are also important factors, as is intellectual capability.[17]

## D. Expectations

To a surprising degree, we derive from experience that which we anticipate, and we live out our expectations of ourselves. The diversity of response to drugs is at least partially accounted for by the fact that many of the drugs cause dissociation. Once the always tenuous restraints of reality are further released it is not difficult to see why events follow closely after the heart of desire or apprehension. The "revealed" state once experienced can produce a permanent conversion.

## E. Physiological State

Hunger, sleep deprivation and reduced oxygen supply brought on by retarded breathing (as in Yoga) usually accentuate the speed and depth of drug action. Reportedly, elevated blood sugar provides an extra depth of response with certain drugs (e.g. marihuana). The general state of nutrition, recent diet, the presence or absence of other drugs even, at times, those used months before[18] may alter responses. There are curious combinations. The use of Calabar beans in ritual trials is based on the fact that in the presence of high adrenalin the drug is poisonous, but otherwise is relatively harmless.

Thus alterations in physiological states can determine the extent of a drug response and whether it will have any long-term or even short-term effects.

### F. *Timing*

One of the most basic of biological phenomena is the constant waxing and waning in addition to diurnal rhythms. Lack of appropriate techniques for measuring, storing and analyzing such data led in the past to serious neglect of this problem. High speed data collection techniques and computers with large enough memory cores have brought us within sights of dealing with this area, although the soft-ware (i.e. the programs) for analysis are still generally lacking.

Timing is crucial in at least three ways:

1. When in the life cycle the drug is given, i.e. there are often specified periods, prenatal as well as postpartum, when, and only when, the fetus or neonate is susceptible.
2. The effect of a drug on a specific parameter or even the total organism may differ depending on whether that specific parameter is ebbing or flowing. This in turn may determine whether there is or is not a permanent alteration in the life pattern.
3. For some, but not all drugs, the time of day has been shown to strongly affect the response.

### III. PROBABLE FUTURE ALTERATIONS OF LIFE PATTERNS BY DRUGS

Implication of the future directions in which drug usage is likely to go already exist in a substantial number of the pharmaceuticals presently available. Some of these are currently regarded as "side effects," but it is almost an aphorism that "today's side effects are tomorrow's therapy." The shortened sleep need with monoamine oxidase inhibitors, the reduced sexual sensitivity or even the shortened memory span have, each of them, possible therapeutic applications. The real problems in the field of psychopharmaceuticals is not so much the creation of any of the following classes of drugs (see Table 6-III) but determining who should make the decisions as to when they should be used, on whom and by whom.

TABLE 6-III

PROBABLE FUTURE ALTERATIONS OF LIFE PATTERNS BY DRUGS

1. Prolong Childhood and (Shorten?) Adolescence
2. Reduce Need for Sleep
3. Provide Safe, Short-acting Intoxicants
4. Regulate Sexual Responses
5. Control Affect and Aggression
6. Mediate Nutrition, Metabolism and Physical Growth
7. Increase or Decrease Reactivity (Alertness, Relaxation)
8. Prolong or Shorten Memory
9. Induce or Prevent Learning
    a. Experience without reinforcement
    b. Vicariously with reinforcement
10. Produce or Discontinue Transference
11. Provoke or Relieve Guilt
12. Foster or Terminate Mothering Behavior
13. Shorten or Extend Experienced Time
14. Create Conditions of *j'amais vu* (Novelty) *or deja vu* (Familiarity)
15. Deepen our Awareness of Beauty and our Sense of Awe

Unquestionably additional and probably even more startling drug actions will occur as fall-out from other research in the field. As newer possibilities occur and as we gain experience with those already available or possible, there is also likely to be a shift in attitude in respect to this most important question of whom shall exercise control.

## A.  *Prolong Childhood and (Shorten?) Adolescence*

The average human life span has been greatly prolonged in the past century, but this occurred primarily by the reduction in infant mortality and the reduction of deaths from pneumonia in the older age groups. Unfortunately there is little we can do to reverse or prevent the depredations of aging. Even in the best of health the years beyond "three score year and ten" are not usually one's best.

One of the features which has made human civilization possible is the prolonged childhood of man, since it is then that he is most susceptible to education. It has been this vastly extended period as compared with other animals that has been a unique feature of the human venture. Hence it would appear sensible to try to prolong life another few decades by extending the period during which the acquisition of knowledge and skills comes most easily. We are already doing this in a social sense since the time at which one finishes college is already half a dozen years beyond physical maturity.

Conceivably if childhood were adequate the turbulence of adolescence could be short-circuited with avoidance of many of the problems which thereafter continue to plague people in later life.

### B.  Reduce Need for Sleep

As previously indicated this has already occurred as a side effect of some of the antidepressant drugs. Based on the rigorous training of the Mogul Emperors, as well as current physiological evidence, it appears entirely possible that three to three and a half hours sleep is all that is really required. The habit of sleeping longer quite possibly developed as a survival trait, since it was not safe for a creature such as man with such poor night vision, along with his other inadequacies, to go wandering about at a time of day when he was so poorly protected.

With the increasing knowledge of the functions of REM time (Rapid Eye Movement) and the various stages of sleep it now looks as though we may be able to simulate or induce the bioelectric-biochemical activity required and conceivably be able to totally circumvent the need for sleep. Constructive use of these additional billions of man hours every day is indeed a challenge.

### C.  Provide Safe Short-acting Intoxicants

At least under the present rituals and routines in which we live it seems almost essential that periods of relief be provided. Safe, rapidly acting intoxicants that produce satisfactory dissociation and euphoria would be most valuable. The appeal of alcohol, of marihuana, of opiates, amphetamines, etc., is due at least in part, to the fact that they do possess some degree of such activity. However none of them serves ideally for the purpose. It is quite likely that if acknowledgment were given of the desirability of such a pharmaceutical that it could be produced within a matter of a few years at most.

### D. Regulate Sexual Responses

Man is one of the few creatures in whom sexual activity is not seasonal. His constant restlessness on this score provides him with both more pleasures and more problems than any other bodily function. Pharmacological regulation of some aspects of this behavior is already available, and others will probably be achieved in the next few years. Banking the fires or stoking them biochemically so that temperature and activity could match more closely the appropriate environmental circumstances would increase the sum total of pleasure and at the same time allow man to devote more of his time, intelligence and energies to more exclusively human activities.

### E. Control Affect and Aggression

There is some evidence that electrolyte balance is related to control of excessive excursions of affect and aggression. Perhaps the skeptical attitudes of Americans toward balneology and mineral water has been mistaken. Fluoridation of water has been generally accepted as a dental health measure. Why not lithium in the water supply as well if it is capable of preventing pathology without circumscribing normal human feelings?

### F. Mediate Nutrition, Metabolism and Physical Growth

At least as great and possibly greater than psychosomatic effects are the somatopsychic ones. Adequate control of the genetic code or of the messenger functions should enable us within a few decades to eliminate most gross physical pathology so that deviations so extreme as to be regarded as ugly will no longer occur. A great deal of the psychopathology which arises because one human regards himself as physically or aesthetically inferior to another could be eliminated. This type of investigation is already under way.

### G. Increase or Decrease Reactivity (Alertness, Relaxation)

Some of the pharmaceuticals available permit us to extend to a small degree the period of reactivity by deferring fatigue. There are others which partially work to permit relaxation when hyperalertness would only be a nuisance. It is quite possible that appropriate "natural" products (plants, etc.) already exist that would provide the lead towards synthesizing virtually ideal substances for these purposes. Recognition of the need and conscious search would perhaps provide these agents almost at once.

## H. Prolong or Shorten Memory

How much remarkably more rich life would be if we were able to remember whatever we wished. On the other hand, how terribly cruel if we could not forget those things we had seen or done which were unbearable. We are close enough to understanding how memory works to expect that within another decade such agents could become a reality.

## I. Induce or Prevent Learning

1. Experience without reinforcement

There are certain experiences through which one must unavoidably pass that may well scar the organism for an indefinite period. To some degree we do protect ourselves by not incorporating these events into our total psychic organization. In other cases unfortunately we do not have such control. Somewhat improved analyses of the biochemical changes which occur during such states should allow us within the foreseeable future to have available drugs which would prevent fatal flawing.

2. Vicariously with reinforcement

On the other hand, there are both positive and negative experiences which would greatly enhance performance if the "lesson" they had to provide could be learned. Tentative beginnings have already been made in the use of drugs which would enhance the learning capacity of the individual so that the "experience" could be achieved vicariously via movies, reading or being told.

The availability of such inducements to learning would likely alter the total educational process so that the time consumed to acquire any one segment would be greatly reduced and the scope greatly broadened to include "character education" as well.

## J. Produce or Discontinue Transference

The great desire to establish or discontinue transference relationships is overtly evident in primitive societies where the demand for love philters is a high priority item. In only slightly disguised form the use of chemicals as deodorants, mouth washes and perfumes are essentially for the same purpose.

It would undoubtedly be constructed as an invasion of privacy to give *someone else* a pharmaceutical without their knowledge or permission. On the other hand, if one could "turn off," it would no longer be really necessary in most cases to involve the party of the second part. In theory at least there is no reason why the deconditioning experience should not be greatly augmented through the use of appropriate drugs.

The potential uses in terms of psychotherapy with involved oedipal situations presents an almost limitless potential.

## K. Provoke or Relieve Guilt

The biochemical correlates of many of the affective states are being subjected to investigation at the present time. Use of a technique such as that of Delgado[19] should make it possible to directly evaluate not only what such correlates are but whether the introduction of them will in turn produce the emotional state itself. According to one theory at least the whole penal system is directed toward this end. How much simpler life would be if sufficient sense of guilt could be produced relevant to a particular type of situation to prevent its repetition. "Punishment" would then be truly rehabilitative and practically instantaneous.

At other times an undeserved and unwarranted feeling of guilt can ruin an entire life and even those of others touching it. A substantial part of what a psychiatrist does is attempt to relieve such unwarranted and destructive guilt feelings. There is already evidence that this can be done pharmacologically in respect to anxiety which may well be an important component of guilt. Some interesting ethical and legal problems arise so that if such a drug is perfected it may be that a board consisting of a judge and a clergyman as well as a psychiatrist would have to agree that such relief of guilt was justifiable before appropriate medication is given.

### L.   Foster or Terminate Mothering Behavior

With mothering behavior so typical of certain animals it appears highly probable that there are "juices" which mediate in the production of this behavior. By enhancing or interfering with their production it is possible that the extent of such behavior could be controlled. There are cases where an increase of this function would be in order, but undoubtedly the greatest use would be in terminating such behavior once it had outlived its usefulness. The human female gets involved in more difficulties and in turn involves others in problems more because of excess inappropriate mothering behavior than because of untoward sexual passion, or, for that matter, any other emotion.

### M.   Shorten or Extend Experienced Time

Drugs capable of altering our sense of time to some degree at least are already in existence. Jazz musicians credit both marihuana and the opiates with a capacity to extend the experience of time so that both the appreciation and production of music is greatly enhanced. There are various other occupations where this capacity would be quite important, e.g. magicic, ball playing, etc. On the other hand, there are certain experiences which one wishes to have done with as rapidly as possible and any agent which speeded up the passage of experienced time would be useful.

### N.   Create Conditions of J'amais Vu (Novelty) or Deja Vu (Familiarity)

Married life would be considerably altered if one could bring to one's mate the feeling of fresh wonder that often characterizes the initial or early experiences. The same would hold true in many business partnerships and other working relationships. On occasion some of the dissociating drugs do produce some reactions of this sort but are as yet far too crude and unpredictable to be used specifically for this purpose.

It would not do to have all situations or even the majority of them of the "novelty" type. Indeed it is also important to have available a compound which would create a feeling of familiarity in order to more competently deal with problems that are made more difficult simply because they are new. Some of the euphoriant drugs tend in this direction.

## O. Deepen Our Awareness of Beauty and Our Sense of Awe

Finally, by deepening our appreciation of the beauty which surrounds us and allowing us to experience afresh the awe of human existence we can perhaps better discover both emotionally and intellectually the nature of the human venture. It is this type of appeal that has made drugs so familiar an adjunct to religious ecstasies. This usage should be developed with enough improvement in the drugs themselves to insure that the experiences be expansions of reality rather than deceptions into parauniverses.

All of these—and many more to come—are probes into the extension and control of our destinies. There is no more suitable ending than the quotation from Pope's Essay on Man:

> Know then thyself, presume not God to scan,
> The proper study of mankind is Man.
> Placed on this isthmus of a middle state,
> A being darkly wise, and rudely great;
> With too much knowledge for the sceptic side,
> With too much weakness for the stoic's pride,
> He hangs between; in doubt to act or rest;
> In doubt to deem himself a god, or beast;
> In doubt his mind or body to prefer;
> Born but to die, and reasoning but to err;
> Sole judge of truth, in endless error hurl'd:
> The glory, jest and riddle of the world!

### REFERENCES

1. McClearn, G. E., and Rodgers, D. A.: Genetic factors in alcohol preference of laboratory mice. *J Comp Physiol Psychol*, 54:116-119, 1961.
2. Dalton, K.: Ante-natal progesterone and intelligence. *Brit J Psychiat*, 114:1377-1382, 1968.
3. Glusman, M.: Discussion. *Proc Amer Psychopath Ass*, 55:202-204, 1967.
4. Young, W. C.: Prenatal gonadal hormones and behavior in the adult. *Proc Amer Psychopath Ass*, 55:173-183, 1967.
5. Young, W. C.: Patterning of sexual behavior. In Bliss, E. L. (Ed.): *Roots of Behavior*. New York, Hoeber-Harper, 1962, pp. 115-122.
6. DiMascio, A., and Rinkel, M.: In Rinkel, M. (Ed.): *Specific and Nonspecific Factors in Psychopharmacology*. New York, Philosophical Library, 1964, p. 130.

7. Heninger, G.; DiMascio, A., and Klerman, G. L.: Personality factors in variability of response to phenothiazines. *Amer J Psychiat, 121*:1091-1094, 1965.

8. Janke, W.: Über psychische Wirkungen verschiedener Tranquilizer bei gasunden, emotional labilen Personen. *Psychopharmacologia, 8*:340-374, 1966.

9. Janke, W.: On the dependence of the effect of psychotropic substances on the affective stability. *Med Exp (Basel), 2*:217-223, 1960.

10. Klerman, G. L.: Transactions of the Sixth Research Conference on Cooperative Chemotherapy Studies in Psychiatry, *6*:339, 1961.

11. Lienert, G. A., and Traxel, W.: The effects of meprobamate and alcohol on galvanic skin response. *J Psychol, 48*:329-334, 1959.

12. Luoto, K.: Personality and placebo effects upon timing behavior. *J Abnorm Soc Psychol, 68*:54-61, 1964.

13. McPeake, J. D., and DiMascio, A.: Drug-personality interaction in the learning of a nonsense syllable task. *Psychol Rep, 15*:405-406, 1964.

14. Munkelt, P., and Othmer, E.: Der Einfluss der psychischen Stabilität resp. Labilität und der Körpe-konstitution der Versuchspersonen auf die Wirkung des Psychotonicums 7-[2'-(1''-Methyl-2''-phenyl-aethylamino)-aethyl]-theophyllin HCl. *Arzneimittelforschung, 15*:843-849, 1965.

15. Nowlis, V., and Nowlis, H. H.: The description and analysis of mood. *Ann N Y Acad Sci, 65*:345-355, 1956.

16. Shagass, C.: In Uhr, L., and Miller, J. G. (Eds.): *Drugs and Behavior.* New York, Wiley, 1969, p. 339.

17. Rickels, K.: Some comments on non-drug factors in psychiatric drug therapy. *Psychosomatics, 8*:303-309, 1965.

18. Esser, A. H., and Kline, N. S.: Routine blood pressure measurement in psychiatric research. *J Clin Pharmacol, 7* (No. 3):162-167, 1967.

19. Delgado, J.: *Salmon Lecture.* New York Academy of Medicine, 1969. In Press.

# 7

## PSYCHEDELIC LSD RESEARCH

ALBERT A. KURLAND, WALTER N. PAHNKE, SANFORD UNGER,
CHARLES SAVAGE, AND STANISLAV GROF

$A$T THIS POINT in time, the future of psychedelic LSD research appears clouded with uncertainties. This seems to have come about largely in the wake of:

1. the popular dramatization of the effects of LSD with an alleged illicit use reaching such proportions that LSD has become principally identified as a drug of abuse.
2. reports of "chromosomal damage" and other physical dangers associated with the use especially of "black market" LSD.
3. the decreasing number of studies being initiated, in good part as a consequence of the notoriety attending the drug.
4. a dearth of investigators who have had first hand clinical or research experience with LSD and the difficulty of obtaining such training.

Confronted with obstacles of this magnitude, it might appear that the demise of human LSD research is imminent. Yet, after considerable experience we are as intrigued as ever

Note: Based on a presentation made by Dr. Kurland at the Seventh Annual Meeting of the American College of Neuropsychopharmacology in San Juan, Puerto Rico, December 16-18, 1968, and a contribution to the Symposium on Psychedelic Drugs at the American Medical Association Annual Convention in New York City, July 17, 1969, by Dr. Pahnke. Research described in these pages was or is being supported, in part, under Public Health Grants No. MH-13747-PY, MH-15555-01, MH-08474, MH-11001 and FR-05546. Appreciation is gratefully acknowledged to the Depts. of Surgery and Psychiatry of the Sinai Hospital, Baltimore, Md., where the cancer project was conducted with the collaboration of Louis Goodman, M.D. Part of this essay has already been published and is reprinted here in part with permission from the *Journal of the American Medical Association*.

about the clinical promise, and hope that the hue and cry over abuse will give way to a resurgence of careful and informed research.

## I. BACKGROUND

In the mid-1950's, Osmond introduced the term "psychedelic" into the scientific literature (1957). The "psychotomimetic" definition of LSD, in his view, had too-narrowly proscribed the fields of inquiry which LSD-type drugs could open. He affirmed: "If mimicking mental illness were the main characteristic of these agents, psychotomimetics would indeed be a suitable generic term. It is true that they may do so, but they do much more."

Hence came the designation "psychedelic," meaning mind-manifesting. In this conception deriving most directly from human studies, the basic data were constituted by verbal descriptions or reports of drug-altered subjective experience. This feature has continued to distinguish the "psychedelic" approach, viz. its primary focus on changes in dimensions or contents of conscious experience in human patients or subjects. From the very first, in contradistinction to "psychotomimetic" studies, psychedelic research incorporated the possibility that positive results might follow the sensitive administration of LSD. Again, Osmond provided the point of departure making the first reference to "the psychedelic use of LSD" in the treatment of alcoholic patients. "Our work started," he said, "with the idea that a single overwhelming experience might be beneficial to alcoholics, this idea springing from [William] James (1902) and [others]."

Over the following few years, several groups of clinical investigators published claims of beneficial results deriving from one or another variant of the psychedelic treatment approach with alcoholics (Chwelos et al., 1959; Smith, 1959; MacLean et al., 1961; O'Reilly and Reich, 1962; Ditman et al., 1962; Jensen, 1962; Savage et al., 1962; and Sherwood et al., 1962). The published reports sometimes seemed elusive and enigmatic with regard to the actual nature of the treatment process and the mechanism or mechanisms of its reputed effects. Hoffer,

(1960), for instance, spoke of the occurrence of "transcendental experiences" induced by the high-dose LSD procedure. Savage, for another instance, wrote as follows:

> Our conception is that [alcoholics] live an inauthentic existential modality (i.e. alienation), and that illness arises from an inability to see meaning in life. LSD may provide an encounter which brings a sudden liberation from ignorance and illusion, enlarges the spiritual horizon and gives a new meaning to life. (1962).

It was at about this time, in 1963, in conference with Jonathan Cole, then Chief of the NIMH Psychopharmacology Service Center, that we operationalized a research effort in this problem area. Cole's attitude, incidentally, was subsequently expressed as follows: "Some of the therapeutic claims made for these drugs are of sufficient potential importance to warrant serious, unprejudiced study" (Cole and Katz, 1964). Hence, with NIMH support, explorations were initiated with patients hospitalized in the Alcoholic Rehabilitation Unit of the Spring Grove State Hospital.

The work at Spring Grove was preceded by a thorough review of the literature (see Unger, 1963), as well as systematic observations of ongoing clinical LSD research in the United States (and later in Europe). The extent to which nonpharmacological, or extradrug, factors could affect the course and character of reactions to LSD had been clearly revealed in earlier investigations. More specifically—beyond the dosage variable—the predominant ideational and affective content, even the very fact of occurrence or nonoccurrence of certain kinds of reactions, as well as the quality and degree of ideational and emotional integration that marked the "reentry"—that is, the return from the "bedrugged" to a "normal" state—all were apparently highly responsive to, if not critically determined by, differences in the mode or manner of preparation, including the structuring of expectations, the premapping of the nature and significance of possible drug-induced experiences, and procedures of programming and guidance during the period of drug action.

From the outset, and throughout, we have maintained a

posture of caution and respect with regard to the impact of LSD on psychological functioning. Actually, the drug has not been administered to a patient in our setting unless and until it was judged that the prospect of clinically beneficial outcome, within the limits of our understanding, had been reasonably maximized. During the LSD session itself, averaging ten to fourteen hours in duration, the patient's therapist, expressly trained and supervised in the use of LSD, and trained nurse remain in constant and continuous attendance—providing immediate support, direction, and interpretation.

## II. EFFECTS IN MAN FACILITATED BY PSYCHEDELIC DRUGS

Before we turn to a broader description of the use of psychedelic drugs as a therapeutic tool let us review briefly some basic facts. It is important to remember that psychedelic drugs are a special class of psychopharmacological agents, not to be confused with sedatives like barbiturates or alcohol, stimulants like amphetamines or methylphenidate HCl (Ritalin®), tranquilizers like chlordiazepoxide HCl (Librium®) or meprobamate (Miltown®), antipsychotic agents like the phenothiazines, or narcotic drugs like the opiates—whether synthetic or natural. Psychedelic drugs, in contrast to true narcotics, are not physically addicting and produce quite different psychological experiences from all these other groups of drugs.

What makes psychedelic drugs unique as a class are the psychological phenomena which they facilitate. Five major kinds of potential psychedelic drug experiences have been described in detail with examples elsewhere (Pahnke and Richards, 1966; Pahnke, 1967) and will only briefly be summarized here.

First is the *psychotic psychedelic experience* characterized by intense fear to the point of panic, paranoid delusions of suspicion or grandeur, toxic confusion, depersonalization, isolation, and/or somatic discomfort; all of these can be of powerful magnitude.

Second is the *cognitive psychedelic experience* characterized by lucidity and novel perspectives. The inner relationships of many levels or dimensions of a problem may be seen all at once. The "creative experience" may have elements in common with this kind of psychedelic experience, but such a possibility awaits the results of future investigation.

Third is the *aesthetic psychedelic experience* characterized by alterations in and intensification of all sensory modalities. Fascinating changes in perception may occur: synesthesia in which sounds can be "seen," objects such as flowers or stones appearing to pulsate and become "alive," ordinary things seemingly imbued with great beauty, music assuming an incredible emotional power, and eyes-closed "visions" of beautiful scenes, intricate geometric patterns, architectural forms, historical events, etc.

Fourth is the *psychodynamic psychedelic experience* characterized by a dramatic emergence into consciousness of material that has previously been unconscious or preconscious. Abreaction and catharsis are elements of what may subjectively be experienced as an actual reliving of incidents from the past or a symbolic portrayal of important conflicts.

The fifth and last type of psychedelic experience has been called by various names: *psychedelic peak, cosmic, transcendental,* or *mystical,* and can be summarized under the following six major psychological characteristics (described in more detail elsewhere, see Pahnke and Richards, 1966):

1. Sense of unity or oneness (positive ego transcendence, loss of usual sense of self without loss of consciousness).
2. Transcendence of time and space.
3. Deeply felt positive mood (joy, peace, and love).
4. Sense of awesomeness and reverence.
5. Meaningfulness of psychological and/or philosophical insight.
6. Ineffability (sense of difficulty in communicating the drug experience by verbal description).

### III.   THE VARIETIES OF PSYCHEDELIC DRUG THERAPIES

In the course of experimental therapeutic work with psychedelic drugs (especially LSD), three major approaches have been tried: (a) psycholytic therapy, (b) psychedelic-chemo-therapy, and (c) psychedelic-peak therapy. Each of these methods was described and discussed in detail at the international conference on LSD therapy held in 1965 (Abramson, 1967). It is essential to keep in mind the differences in procedure among the various methods, not only because different kinds of experiences are facilitated, but also because differing or even conflicting results can be correlated with the particular procedure employed. Reactions to LSD invariably involve a complex interaction between drug dosage, set, and setting.

In psycholytic therapy, which is practiced mainly in Europe, the aim is usually the uncovering of unconscious material which can be psychodynamically analyzed both at the time and in subsequent psychotherapy sessions. There is considerable time spent on psychotherapy before, during, and after the actual drug sessions. This type of therapy is relatively long-term with multiple sessions over time and usually with small doses of the drug (25 to 200 micrograms).

In psychedelic-chemotherapy, the major emphasis is on the psychedelic drug session itself, during which psychotherapy may or may not be carried out. There is minimal preparation and follow-up therapy. A single session with a relatively high dose of the drug (200 micrograms or more) has been the usual practice, although there have been experiments giving weekly sessions with little or no attempt at help with interpretation or integration. This method is called hypnodelic when hypnotic induction is employed during the preparation for the session and/or just before the onset of drug effects with the aim of providing better control. The major differences between psychedelic-chemotherapy and psycholytic therapy are number of drug sessions, amount of therapy outside the drug sessions, and drug dosage.

In psychedelic-peak therapy, one of the distinctive characteristics and immediate goals in the drug session itself is the achievement of a peak or transcendental experience, but just as important is the intensive psychotherapy which occurs in the weeks prior to the psychedelic drug session and the follow-up therapy in the weeks after the session to help with the work of integration. The LSD session can add meaningful emotional insight and dramatic validation of an individual's basic self-worth but only after the achievement of psychodynamic resolution and self-understanding during the preparatory psychotherapy. This preparation—which averages about twenty hours per patient—enables the therapist to establish close rapport with the patient and to gain intimate knowledge of the patient's developmental history, dynamics, defenses, and difficulties. In specific preparation for the session itself the patient is encouraged to let go voluntarily of his usual ego controls and be carried by the experience. Psychedelic-peak therapy is similar to psychedelic-chemotherapy in number of drug sessions (usually 1) and relatively high drug dosages (usually 300 to 500 micrograms of LSD), but resembles psycholytic therapy in the amount of psychotherapy surrounding the actual drug session.

The experimental drug sessions are carried out in special treatment suites furnished like comfortable living rooms with sofas, easy chairs, rugs, pictures, flowers, and high fidelity music equipment. The patient's therapist and a psychiatric nurse are in constant attendance throughout the period of drug action. For most of the session, the patient reclines on the sofa, alternately listening to carefully selected music or interacting with his therapist. The function of the music is both to serve as a "carriage," helping the patient to enter more fully into his unfolding inner world of experience, and to facilitate the release of intense emotionality. The therapist stays closely in touch with the patient's progress throughout the course of the session.

Although the LSD session itself is only one part of psychedelic peak therapy, it plays a unique and necessary role without which the total therapeutic impact would not be the same. In a dosage of 200 mcgms or more, LSD produces a ten to twelve hour period of striking, varied, and anomalous mental functioning; the range of possible effects and/or episodes of reaction is multiform. Certain dimensions of possible reactivity are therapeutically irrelevant (e.g. sensory changes); others have distinctly antitherapeutic consequences (e.g. panic, terror, or psychotic reactions). The major dimension of therapeutic relevance of drug-altered reactivity is the affective or emotional sphere; intense, labile, personally-meaningful emotionality is uniformly produced with periodic episodes of overwhelming feeling. After the third to fifth hours, when psychedelic peak reactivity may be expected to appear, with skillful handling the remainder of the session may be stabilized in an elevated mood state in which psychotic and other turbulent phenomena are most unlikely. Follow-up therapy begins during the reentry period of the session day and continues the next day as the patient and therapist review the events of the session and attempt to consolidate and integrate them. The patient is encouraged to write up a detailed description of his experience.

If a psychedelic-peak experience has been achieved and stabilized during the session, a clinical picture which we have termed the psychedelic afterglow can be observed in the days after the session. Mood is elevated and energetic, there is a relative freedom from concerns of the past, from guilt and anxiety, and the disposition and capacity to enter into close interpersonal relationships is enhanced. These feelings generally persist for from two weeks to a month and then gradually fade into vivid memories that hopefully will still influence attitude and behavior. During the immediate postdrug period there is a unique opportunity for effective psychotherapeutic work on strained family or other interpersonal relationships.

It should be emphasized, however, that even with optimal programming peak experiences are neither universally achieved nor stabilized, and certainly they do not automatically occur merely by administration of a psychedelic drug. In our research setting, profound or marked psychedelic-peak reactions were judged to have occurred in 68 percent of eighty-two consecutive alcoholic patients who received a total dose of 450 micrograms of LSD administered in two stages.

## IV. RESEARCH PROJECTS WITH PSYCHEDELIC-PEAK PSYCHOTHERAPY

As indicated, since 1963 at the Spring Grove State Hospital and now continuing at the Maryland Psychiatric Research Center, research has been in progress investigating the usefulness of psychedelic-peak psychotherapy with alcoholic (Kurland et al., 1966; 1967), neurotic (Unger et al., 1968), narcotic addict, and dying cancer patients (Kurland et al., 1968; Pahnke et al., 1969). The alcoholic and neurotic projects, both funded by NIMH research grants, were designed as double-blind, controlled studies. In each project, on a double-blind basis, the experimental group received a relatively high dose of LSD (350 to 450 mcgms.) in contrast to only 50 micrograms for the control group; both groups received exactly the same therapeutic preparation. In the neurotic study there was an additional comparison group of randomly assigned patients who received an equivalent number of hours of *group* psychotherapy without any LSD. Evaluation of each patient's status was performed by an independent rating team pretreatment and at six, twelve, and eighteen months following the treatment phase. Full and final analysis and evaluation of data are still in progress.

Results are now completed at the six-month checkpoint for the alcoholic study in a total of 135 alcoholic patients who were treated with psychedelic psychotherapy. While the study design made it possible for the patients to have up to three sessions, the vast majority in both experimental and control groups (total of 117 patients) received only one treatment with LSD. The eighteen patients who had more than one LSD session were not found to be different from the other 117 in psychological and social parameters based on pretreatment testing, but as a group they received more average hours of treatment. Therefore, in the interests of uniformity concerning amount of treatment, results were analyzed separately for the 117 patients who had only one LSD session (either a high or low dose). Out of these 117 patients, 104 were personally located for follow-up interview at six months. It should be noted that the thirteen patients not reached for follow-up were properly proportioned according to the original random assignment in which two-thirds of the patients were allotted to the high dose procedure.

Comparison of means pretreatment and six-months posttreatment for global adjustment and drinking behavior are shown in Table 7-I. Global adjustment included occupational, inter-

TABLE 7-I

LSD ALCOHOLIC STUDY: SIX-MONTH RESULTS
PATIENTS RECEIVING ONE LSD SESSION

*Comparison of Means*

I. Means of Global Adjustment and Drinking Behavior Ratings Pretreatment and Six Months Posttreatment for High and Low Dose Groups and Psychedelic Reactivity Groups. The end points of the scale measuring drinking are 0, indicating daily alcohol consumption, and 10, indicating total abstinence.

| Patient Group | Global Adjustment | | Drinking Behavior | |
|---|---|---|---|---|
| | Pre | Six-Month | Pre | Six-Month |
| High Dose (N = 64) | 4.16 | 6.52 | 2.83 | 7.02 |
| Low Dose (N = 40) | 3.28 | 5.13 | 2.93 | 5.75 |
| Profound (N = 23) | 4.43 | 7.13 | 2.65 | 7.52 |
| Marked (N = 31) | 3.87 | 6.16 | 2.94 | 6.94 |
| Minimal (N = 50) | 3.50 | 5.34 | 2.92 | 5.82 |

II. Results of Covariance Analyses For Above Data.

| | Global Adjustment | | Drinking Behavior | |
|---|---|---|---|---|
| | F | $p^*$ | F | $p^*$ |
| High Dose vs. Low Dose | 3.76 | 0.05 | 4.43 | 0.025 |
| Psychedelic Reactivity Groups | 2.42 | 0.05 | 3.09 | 0.025 |

\* p values are for one-tailed tests of significance.

personal, and residential factors as well as the patient's reaction to alcohol. Ratings were made on each patient on a predetermined zero to ten behavior rating scale. The end points of the scale measuring drinking behavior were zero, indicating daily alcohol consumption, and ten indicating total abstinence. Patients were also categorized according to whether a profound, marked, or minimal psychedelic-peak experience was achieved during the LSD session as rated by the patient's therapist immediately postsession. In Table 7-I, comparison of means pre- and posttreatment between high vs. low dose and among the psychedelic reactivity groups may be seen to show statistically significant differences using an analysis of covariance statistical procedure (one-tailed test).

The percentage of patients functioning in an "essentially rehabilitated" fashion is shown for the various groups in Table 7-11. A score of eight or more on the zero to ten scale was

TABLE 7-II

LSD ALCOHOLIC STUDY: SIX-MONTH RESULTS
PATIENTS RECEIVING ONE LSD SESSION

*Percentage of Patients "Rehabilitated"*

I. Percentage of Patients in High and Low Dose Groups and Psychedelic
   Reactivity Groups Obtaining Scores of 8, 9, or 10 on the Global Adjustment
   and Drinking Behavior Scales at Six Months Follow-up. A score of 8 on the
   Drinking Scale indicates departure from total abstinence, but minimally.

| Patient Group | Global Adjustment Scores of 8, 9, or 10 | Drinking Behavior Scores of 8, 9, or 10 |
|---|---|---|
| High Dose (N = 64) | 44% | 53% |
| Low Dose (N = 40) | 25% | 33% |
| Profound (N = 23) | 61% | 61% |
| Marked (N = 31) | 39% | 48% |
| Minimal (N = 50) | 24% | 36% |

II. $X^2$ Results For Above Data.

| | Global Adjustment | | Drinking Behavior | |
|---|---|---|---|---|
| | $X^2$ | $p^*$ | $X^2$ | $p^*$ |
| High vs. Low Dose | 2.97 | 0.05 | 3.44 | 0.05 |
| Psychedelic Reactivity Groups | 9.32 | 0.01 | 5.50 | 0.10 (N.S.) |

   * (p values are for one-tailed tests of significance.)

considered a rigorous criterion, indicating for global adjustment
that a patient was making "good attainment or adjustment" with
regard to drinking, occupation, interpersonal relations, etc. A
score of eight on the drinking scale indicated some, but only
minimal, departure from total abstinence. Statistical analysis
revealed that there were significant differences between the high
and low dose groups in percentage of patients reaching this
criterion, both in global adjustment and on the scale measuring
drinking. The group of patients with the most profound psychedelic-peak experiences had the highest percentage of patients
who showed evidence of rehabilitation. This trend was statistically significant among the three psychedelic reactivity groups
for global adjustment, but not for drinking.

In evaluating these findings in practical terms, we can say
that a given alcoholic patient receiving a single high dose of
LSD in the context of psychedelic-peak psychotherapy and
experiencing a profound psychedelic peak reaction has the best
likelihood for improvement six months later.

The project investigating the effect of psychedelic-peak
psychotherapy with narcotic addicts is well underway, but it is
too early for any indication of therapeutic outcome. These
patients in general seem to have a greater degree of psycho-

pathology than the alcoholics with whom we have worked, but the skilled implementation of psychedelic psychotherapy seems to be proceeding smoothly. An observation of interest is that the character of the drug experience with LSD has been reported by the addicts to be distinctly and qualitatively different from what they experienced under heroin (i.e. a confrontation with their problems rather than an escape from them).

During the past several years, we have also been exploring the potential of psychedelic-peak psychotherapy with cancer patients. The purpose has been to treat the depression, anxiety, psychological isolation and intractable pain which so many of these patients face. The families, too, must cope with psychological problems which relate to their own fears and impending sense of loss. The problem of relating to the patient and telling him about his diagnosis further complicates what is already a grim situation. This use of LSD is similar to that already outlined, except that not quite as much time is spent in preparation and the treatment takes place in a private room of a general medical facility (Sinai Hospital in Baltimore). Also, family therapy plays a larger role.

Thus far we have treated thirty-five patients in a pilot project. Our findings must remain only suggestive at this point, but they do give some promising indications of the potential of this form of treatment. Measurements pre- and post-LSD on depression, anxiety, emotional tension, psychological isolation, fear of death and amount of pain medication required have shown change in a positive direction in about two-thirds of the patients. In half of these the improvement was dramatic, and those patients who had the most profound peak experiences tended to show the most benefit. Also, patients treated earlier in the course of their disease were able to use the experience most rewardingly.

While not all patients were helped dramatically, none—even the most ill—appeared to have been harmed. This finding in regard to the safety of the procedure has been consistent with our results in alcoholic and neurotic patients.

The following case summary will serve to illustrate the method and possible outcome:

The patient, a fifty-eight year old, Jewish, married female, had suffered from cancer of the breast for twelve years. In spite of numerous surgical and medical procedures including hysterectomy, ovarectomy, and adrenalectomy, the disease had spread widely in her spine. At the time she was referred for LSD treatment, pressure on nerves in her spine had caused numbness and a paralysis of the lower half of her body. When first interviewed, the patient was anxious and depressed.

After six hours of preparatory psychotherapy with the patient and her family over the period of a week during which the nature and purpose of the treatment was explained, the patient was given 300 micrograms of LSD. The first few hours of her psychedelic session went well and were pleasant, but a complete psychedelic peak experience was not obtained. There were a few moments of intense positive psychedelic reactivity, for example, at one point the patient exclaimed, "This is one of the happiest days of my life. I will always remember it." There were also transient episodes of apprehension, confusion, and paranoia which were easily handled by reassurance and support.

During the latter part of the session, the patient raised the question of whether or not she would walk again. This issue was handled by a realistic review of the patient's condition, and the therapist finally stated in a direct answer to her question that it was very unlikely that she would be able to walk again. The patient then expressed her reluctant acceptance of the idea that her life could still go on even if she were confined to bed, a condition which she had previously greatly feared. However, the patient spontaneously expressed her determination to try her best in physiotherapy, in spite of the odds against her. She was supported in her resolve to try, but also discussed was acceptance of her condition, if it could not be improved. During the evening after the patient had emerged from the effects of the drug, the patient's family visited. This was a time of intense closeness and interpersonal sharing. The family remarked on a change in her attitude from anxiety and depression to peace and joy.

In the days after the session the patient's mood was cheerful and hopeful. Upon discharge from the hospital six days after her LSD treatment, the patient returned home and began intensive work with a physiotherapist. She made remarkable, quite unexpected progress and within four months was able to use a walker. Six months after treatment the patient was doing some limited walking with a cane.

In spite of her impressive accomplishments, the patient again became depressed and difficult to manage at home because of her feelings that she would always be an invalid. She was especially distressed because the backbrace which she had to wear out of bed (4 to 6 hours a day) was cumbersome and she needed assistance by another person in order to put it on. Because of her increasing depression, both the patient and her family requested another LSD treatment. She was seen regularly for preparation. Interpersonal relations, her self-concept, and some realistic expectations for the future were the major issues explored.

Ten months after her first session the patient was readmitted to the hospital for her second LSD treatment. Her initial reaction to the session was one of anxiety, and then the issue of her disease was encountered. She faced the fact that throughout her illness she had tended to deny that she was really sick. She remembered patients she had known with cancer, and her fear of decaying flesh was symbolized by visions of vultures feeding on rotten meat. After confronting—rather than retreating from—these unpleasant feelings and experiences, the patient had the experience of passing through a series of blue curtains or veils. On the other side she felt as if she were a bird in the sky soaring through the air. Then she was on a high mountain top in a small cabin alone with the snow falling. She experienced wonderful feelings of peace and harmony and visions of beautiful colors like the rainbow. After this, she stabilized the experiences and had enjoyable reliving of happy memories from her past—the best of which was her wedding day, which she relived in great detail including a reexperience of the way her mother sighed as she came down the aisle. These happy memories were in contrast to the early part of her experience when she had relived some unpleasant events, such as the prejudice she felt against her as a child because she was Jewish, and her failure to take advantage of the cultural opportunities her father had provided. In the latter part of the experience the patient thought deeply about her family while looking at their pictures. She was able to resolve some of the ambivalence she had about her younger daughter who was to be married in three months. She felt sorry for some of the strife they had had and came out of the experience with a resolve to make a more constructive attempt to relate to this girl in the future. When the patient's family arrived after supper, she had a serene smile on her face, but was reluctant to talk about her experience too much. She said, "You wouldn't believe me if I did tell you."

Subsequently, the patient left the hospital in good spirits and was able to participate actively in her daughter's wedding. She fulfilled her desire to walk down the aisle without the aid of even a cane, and during the wedding reception she amazed all the guests by dancing with her husband. Her sister said she was the life of the party.

Within six months the patient requested a third LSD treatment. At this time she had increasing pain and was discouraged because she had not worked in over two years, although she had kept the hope alive that she would eventually return to her old job. The session began smoothly but the patient became frightened when she saw a huge wall of flames. After support and encouragement by the therapist the patient was able to go through the middle of the flames, and at this point experienced positive ego transcendence. She felt that she had left her body, was in another world, and was in the presence of God which seemed symbolized by a huge diamond-shaped iridescent Presence. She did not see Him as a Person but knew He was there. The feeling was one of awe and reverence, and she was filled with a sense of peace and freedom. Because she was free from her body, she felt no pain at all. She was quiet during most of the day and emerged from the session with a deep feeling of peace and joy. When her family had arrived, she radiated a psyche-delic afterglow of peace and beauty which all remarked upon. During the course of the evening the patient had a serious talk with her daughters about her condition and what might lie ahead. Shortly thereafter, the patient was discharged from the hospital in good spirits. One effect of the treatment was that when the patient was troubled with pain, she could push the pain out of her mind by remembering her out-of-the-body LSD experience.

The patient did very well for about one month until she slipped on the stairs one day and injured her back which began causing her considerable pain again. She also became sick with the flu and was confined to bed. Prior to this she had been considering going back to work at her old job, part-time, but with the worsening of her physical condition these plans had to be postponed. With these physical setbacks and especially the recurrence of her pain, the patient again became somewhat depressed. Both the patient and her family requested another LSD treatment. The patient was seen for about a month as an outpatient, and then readmitted for LSD, almost six months after her third treatment.

The evening before her session, during the final preparation, the patient suddenly asked a direct question about her diagnosis for the first time in the almost two years she had been in the LSD treatment program. Although she knew that her breast had been removed for cancer, she had believed there was no further growth, but her increasing back pain had made her wonder. Her questions were answered gently, but without evasion, and the meaning and emotional impact were discussed with her. The family members were informed of this conversation immediately thereafter, and they reacted by becoming quite upset and angry. That very evening, in a general family discussion, with the patient and therapist, however, most of them were able to resolve their feelings. Some felt embarrassed because of their previous pretense; most felt relieved when they saw how well the patient had dealt with the situation. The patient stated that she was glad to know the truth and was obviously not psychologically shattered or further depressed as some of the family members had feared.

The fourth session the next day went smoothly, except for some nausea which was a reliving of an episode the patient had experienced shortly before admission when she had eaten some spoiled food. Much psychodynamic material emerged concerning her feelings about various members of her family—especially her two daughters. In the evening the patient felt very close to her family and spent some time in talking to each of them alone in a very personal way. She was reluctant to have them leave at the end of the evening, even though she was very tired. In the days after the session the patient felt relaxed and in good spirits. She was not pessimistic about the future, in spite of the new knowledge about her diagnosis of metastatic cancer to the spine. She was able to tolerate her back pain with the aid of narcotic drugs, but did not have complete pain relief.

While still in the hospital, a hypophysectomy was attempted as a possible means to stop further spread of her metastatic process. Because of hemorrhage the operation could not be completed, and the patient died a few days later.

This patient experienced considerable relief from pain, depression, and anxiety over the period of almost two years, during which she received four LSD treatments. Her first session was not judged to have had much psychedelic content, but the second, third, and fourth sessions did. The third session was the most complete psychedelic peak experience and seemed to provide the most benefit. This patient's gratifying physical improvement can be attributed only indirectly to the LSD treatment in that her own underlying resolution to pursue physiotherapy emerged when her depression and anxiety were relieved. By a fortunate coincidence her condition responded well to these efforts on her part, contrary to the most informed medical prognosis. All of our patients are told that LSD is used for treatment of psychological distress and not as a cure for their physical disease. In this case, as happens not infrequently sometime during the course of LSD treatment, the issue of diagnosis was brought up by the patient and had to be worked out with the patient and the family.

## V.  THE QUESTION OF SAFETY

When psychedelic drugs are administered under controlled medical conditions (as has been the case in several large scale research projects in recent years), permanent adverse effects have been quite rare. Since 1963 at the Spring Grove State Hospital, and now at the Maryland Psychiatric Research Center, over three hundred patients have been treated with LSD without a single case of long-term psychological or physical harm directly attributable to the treatment, although there have been two post-LSD disturbances which have subsequently responded to conventional treatment.

Throughout the years of research with LSD many possible harmful physical effects have been suggested, but careful subsequent investigation has failed to furnish much conclusive scientific evidence. Most recently the question of chromosomal damage has been raised following the positive *in vitro* findings in white blood cells of Cohen *et al.* (1967a). Retrospective studies on persons having taken LSD from the black market or under medical supervision have produced conflicting reports. Some researchers (Cohen *et al.*, 1967b; Egozcue *et al.*, 1968; Nielson *et al.*, 1968) found increased chromosomal breakage over normal rates, and others found no increase (Loughman *et al.*, 1967; Bender and Sankar, 1968; Sparks *et al.*, 1968).

Because we were in a position to study the effect of pure LSD of known amount on patients who were to be treated with psychedelic psychotherapy, we entered into collaboration with the cytogenetics laboratory of Dr. J. H. Tjio at the National Institute of Arthritis and Metabolic Diseases to carry out a rigorously controlled study. Blood samples from thirty-two patients being treated at the Spring Grove State Hospital were drawn and cultured pre- and post-LSD. The white blood cell chromosomes were then studied without prior identification of the slides, and at least two hundred metaphases were analyzed per culture. In addition, the white blood cell chromosomes of five chronic LSD users were studied before, during, and after the administration of known doses of LSD in research on sensory, cognitive, and perceptual functions at the National Institutes of Health.

No difference was found in the rate of chromosomal aberrations before and after LSD when the data from these thirty-seven separate individuals were statistically analyzed. Also, post-LSD chromosomal analysis was done on eight normal subjects who had received LSD in research experiments in the past, and no increase over normal chromosomal breakage rate was found. A summary of these results is presented in Table 7-III. The mean

TABLE 7-III

MEANS OF CHROMOSOMAL ABERRATION RATES* BEFORE AND AFTER LSD AMONG VARIOUS EXPERIMENTAL GROUPS

|  | Pre | Post | Difference | p |
|---|---|---|---|---|
| 32 Patients | 4.28 | 5.91 | + 1.63 | n.s.** |
| 5 Users | 2.81 | 3.57 | + 0.76 | n.s.*** |
| 8 Experimental Subjects |  | 2.79 |  |  |
| 2 Normal Subjects | 2.65 |  |  |  |

* Aberration rate = percentage of aberrant cells/total metaphases analyzed (at least 200 per culture).
** = Wilcoxon Matched-Pairs, Signed-Ranks, two-tailed Test.
*** = Fisher Exact Probability Test.

pre-LSD rates in the thirty-two patients (4.28%) and the five LSD users (2.81%) were comparable to each other and to the values obtained from two normal control subjects' samples for eight to ten consecutive days (2.65%). The pre- to post-LSD differences for both the thirty-two patients (+1.63%) and the five LSD users (+0.76%) were not statistically significant. The mean chromosomal aberration rates for the thirty-two patients and five LSD users (including both pre- and post-means), eight experimental LSD subjects (post-LSD), and two normal controls (no LSD) only varied from 2.65 percent to 5.91 percent. Detailed reports of this research have been presented and published (Tijo et al., 1969a and 1969b).

## VI. DISCUSSION

The conflicting results concerning the efficacy of psychedelic drugs as therapeutic tools in the treatment of different categories of mental illness are apparently attributable in good part to the differences in the methods employed by different groups of researchers. Practically each research team has developed or implemented its own distinctive procedure, some of which would seem to have proven unproductive.

In spite of, but in some respects growing out of, this diversity of approach, several points or conclusions appear to have been clarified by now. LSD is not a substitute for skilled psychotherapy. Experiments where LSD was used primarily as a chemotherapy, or with a minimum of psychotherapy, have not shown any greater efficacy of therapeutic outcome, especially with alcoholics, than control groups (Smart and Storm, 1967; Ludwig et al., 1969; Hollister et al., 1969). The weight of evidence and experience from the psycholytic use of LSD by European researchers and psychedelic-peak therapy as practiced at the Maryland Psychiatric Research Center indicates that skilled use of LSD, when integrated or embedded within the matrix of an intensive psychotherapy program can enhance the therapeutic process in important ways.

The scientific evidence concerning possible genetic hazards of LSD is conflicting and inconclusive. The difference in results between our carefully controlled pre-to-post-LSD study on patients and the research on LSD abusers may be explained by the many uncontrolled variables such as viral infections and the effect of other drugs. Certainly much more research is needed in this complex area before valid conclusions can be drawn.

Our view is that future research with psychedelic drugs needs to be continued in order that we may learn to use them even more effectively. Newer psychedelic drugs may have certain advantages over more well-known ones. For example, we have been testing a new compound, DPT (dipropyltryptamine), developed by Szara (1965) at the NIMH, which has a duration of action of from two to four hours depending on dosage. If this drug proves to be as safely manageable as we have found LSD, it could result in a psychedelic procedure that could be more flexibly and easily implemented than that entailed in utilizing the much longer-acting LSD.

Psychedelic drugs are obviously powerful tools and need to be used and handled wisely. In this regard, it may be worthy of note that the Joint PHS-FDA Committee on Research with Psychotomimetic Agents has just recently authorized us to administer LSD training sessions to a sample of scientists and mental health related professionals in the interest primarily of aiding the formulation and conduct of new and diverse research efforts in this area.

## VII.  THE YEAR 2000

In attempting to summarize the significance of the exploratory probes being carried out relative to the use of LSD as an adjunct to psychotherapy, and the beginning exploration of other agents of similar nature, many thoughts occur as to possible future use. One can visualize, thirty years hence, that these techniques may be more generally applied to the individual exhibiting some malignant form of character distortion. In special clinics, LSD-type drugs could be utilized in conjunction with special forms of psychotherapy to resolve those problems which may have led to the abuse of alcohol or narcotic drugs. There is also the possibility that creative individuals, in periods of depression or blockage, will seek facilities where a feeling of renewal can be released. Likewise, the aging patient who finds himself living only a vegetative existence, because of diminishing capacities for participating in the world's activities, may be provided with periodic experiences in which the fading embers of his memories, sensations, feelings and thoughts may be fanned into a warming fire. Stimulation of this nature may carry over for a period of months, increasing comfort, zest, self-acceptance, and the feeling of having lived to the maximum. For those whom death may approach prematurely through some disease process for which no remedy is available, the preparation for dying may be made an experience of meaning and resolution, adding dignity and stature to both the patient and those close to him.

Other possible useful applications of drugs or procedures

which alter consciousness may be for individuals who are subjected to prolonged periods of isolation and separation from the usual daily activities of man, such as long space voyages of the future or assignment to remote communications stations. In such settings, procedures of this nature may induce or facilitate meditative states, allowing for relative freedom from anxiety, but nevertheless making possible fully alert response to any emergency situation.

These are a few of the vistas and dreams that arise out of the experiences and observations of present research. It may even be that this first generation of experimentation may ultimately lead to the discovery and utilization, in a controlled manner, of untapped potentials in the recesses of man's mind.

## REFERENCES

1. Abramson, Harold (Ed.): *The Use of LSD in Psychotherapy and Alcoholism.* New York, Bobbs-Merrill, 1967.
2. Bender, L., and Sankar, D. V. S.: Chromosomal damage not found in leucocytes of children treated with LSD-25. *Science, 159*:749, 1968.
3. Chwelos, Nicholas; Blewett, Duncan; Smith, C., and Hoffer, Abram: Use of LSD-25 in the treatment of alcoholism. *Quart J Stud Alcohol, 20*:577-590, 1959.
4. Cohen, M.; Marinello, M., and Bach, N.: Chromosomal damage in human leucocytes induced by lysergic acid diethylamide. *Science, 155*:1417-19, 1967.
5. Cohen, M.; Hirschhorn, K., and Frosch, W.: *In vivo* and *in vitro* chromosomal damage induced by LSD-25. *New Eng J Med, 227 (No. 20)*:1043-49, 1967.
6. Cole, Jonathan, O., and Katz, Martin M.: The psychotomimetic drugs, an overview. *JAMA, 187*:10, 1964.
7. Ditman, Keith; Hayman, Max, and Whittlesey, John R. B.: Nature and frequency of claims following LSD. *J Nerv Ment Dis, 134*:346-52, 1962.
8. Egozcue, J.; Irwin, S., and Maruffo, C. A.: Chromosomal damage in LSD users. *JAMA, 204*:214-18, 1968.
9. Hoffer, Abram: Group interchange. In Abramson, Harold (Ed.): *The Use of LSD in Psychotherapy: Transactions of a Conference.* New York, Josiah Macy, Jr., Foundation Publications, 1960.
10. Hollister, L. E.; Shelton, J., and Krieger, G.: A controlled comparison of lysergic acid diethylamide (LSD) and dextroamphetamine in alcoholics. *Amer J Psychiat, 125 (No. 10)*:58-63, 1969.

11. James, William: *The Varieties of Religious Experience.* New York, Modern Library, 1902.
12. Jensen, Sven E.: A treatment program for alcoholics in a mental hospital. *Quart J Stud Alcohol, 23:*315-20, 1962.
13. Kurland, A. A.; Shaffer, J., and Unger, S.: Psychedelic psychotherapy (LSD) in the treatment of alcoholism—an approach to a controlled study. *Excerpta Medica International Congress Series, No. 129, Proceedings of the Fifth International Congress of the Collegium Internationale Neuropsychopharmacologicum,* Washington, D. C., 435-440, March 28-31, 1966.
14. Kurland, A. A.; Unger, S.; Shaffer, J., and Savage, C.: Psychedelic therapy utilizing LSD in the treatment of the alcoholic patient: A preliminary report. *Amer J Psychiat, 123 (No. 10):*1202-09, 1967.
15. Kurland, A. A.; Pahnke, W. N.; Unger, S.; Savage, C.; Wolf, S., and Goodman, L.: Psychedelic therapy (utilizing LSD) with terminal cancer patients. *J Psychedelic Drugs, 3 (No. 1):*63-75, 1970.
16. Loughman, W. D.; Sargent, T. W., and Israelstram, D. M.: Leukocytes of humans exposed to lysergic acid diethylamide: Lack of chromosomal damage. *Science, 158:*508-10, 1967.
17. Ludwig, A.; Levine, J.; Spark, L., and Lazar, R.: The clinical study of LSD treatment in alcoholism. *Amer J Psychiat, 126 (No. 1):*59-69, 1969.
18. MacLean, J. Ross; MacDonald, D. C.; Byrne, Ultan P., and Hubbard, A. M.: The use of LSD-25 in the treatment of alcoholism and other psychiatric problems. *Quart J Stud Alcohol, 22:*34-45, 1961.
19. Nielsen, J.; Friedrich, U., and Tsuboi, T.: Chromosome abnormalities and psychotropic drugs. *Nature, 218:*488-89, 1968.
20. O'Reilly, P. O., and Reich, Genevieve: Lysergic acid and the alcoholic. *Dis Nerv Syst, 23:*331-334, 1962.
21. Osmond, Humphrey: A review of the clinical effects of psychotomimetic agents. *Ann N Y Acad Sci, 66:*418-434, 1957.
22. Pahnke, Walter, and Richards, William: Implications of LSD and experimental mysticism. *J Religion Health, 5:*175-208, 1966.
23. Pahnke, Walter: LSD and religious experience. In Leaf, R., and Debold, R. (Eds.): *LSD, Man and Society.* Middletown, Conn., Wesleyan Univ. Press, 1967, pp. 60-84.
24. Pahnke, W.; Kurland, A. A.; Goodman, L. E., and Richards, W. A.: LSD-assisted psychotherapy with terminal cancer patients. In Hicks, R. E., and Fink, P. J. (Eds.): *Psychedelic Drugs.* New York, Grune and Stratton, 1969.
25. Savage, Charles; Terrill, James, and Jackson, Donald D.: LSD, transcendence, and the new beginning. *J Nerv Ment Dis, 135:*425-439, 1962.
26. Sherwood, John N.; Stolaroff, Myron, and Harman, Willis W.: The

psychedelic experience—a new concept in psychotherapy. *J Neuropsychiat,* 3:370-375, 1962.

27. Smart, R. G.; Storm, T.; Baker, E. F., and Solursh, L.: *Lysergic Acid Diethylamide (LSD) in the Treatment of Alcoholism.* Bookside Monograph of the Addiction Research Foundation No. 6, Univ. of Toronto Press, 1967.

28. Smith, Colin M.: Some reflections on the possible therapeutic effects of the hallucinogens. *Quart J Stud Alcohol,* 20:292-301, 1959.

29. Sparkes, R. S.; Melnyk, J., and Bozzetti, L. P.: Chromosomal effect *in vivo* of exposure to lysergic acid diethylamide. *Science,* 160:1343-44, 1968.

30. Szara, S.; Faillace, L. A., and Speck, L. B.: Metabolic and physiological correlates of the psychological reaction to three short-reacting tryptamine derivatives. In Brill, H.; Cole, J., and Deniker, P., *et al.* (Eds.): *Proceedings of the Fifth International Congress of the Collegium Internationale Neuropsychopharmacologicum,* publication 129. International Congress series. Amsterdam, Excerpta Medica Foundation, 1967, p. 115.

31. Tjio, J. M.; Pahnke, W. N., and Kurland, A. A.: Pre- and post-LSD chromosomal aberrations: A comparative study. In Costa, E., and Greengard, P. (Eds.): *Advances in Biochemical Psychopharmacology,* New York, Raven Press, 1969, vol. I, pp. 191-204. Presented at the American College of Neuropsychopharmacology Meeting, December 20, 1968, San Juan, Puerto Rico.

32. Tjio, J. H.; Pahnke, W. N., and Kurland, A. A.: LSD and chromosomes: A controlled study. *JAMA,* 210:849-856, 1969.

33. Unger, Sanford: Mescaline, LSD, psilocybin and personality change: A review. *Psychiatry,* 26:111-125, 1963.

34. Unger, S.; Kurland, A. A.; Shaffer, J. W.; Savage, C.; Wolf, S.; Leihy, R.; McCabe, O., and Shock, H.: LSD-type drugs and psychedelic therapy. Schlien, J. *et al.* (Eds.): *Research in Psychotherapy.* Washington, D. C., Amer Psychol Ass, 1968, vol. III, pp. 521-35.

# 8

## THE USE OF PSYCHOTROPIC DRUGS WITH CRIMINALS

### OSCAR RESNICK

THE STUDY OF criminality is extremely complex and involves the many disciplines of sociology, psychology, and biomedicine. Since the many different types of criminals of all ages exhibit a wide range of behavior patterns, such a discussion becomes very difficult indeed. Therefore, it becomes necessary to develop a simplified scheme to serve as a basis for the examination of the behavioral symptomatologies most frequently associated with criminality—thus allowing for a coherent and, hopefully, lucid discussion of the use of psychotropic drugs with criminals. This simplified scheme is based in large measure on the discussion by Dr. Adolph Jonas[1] in his classic book entitled the *Ictal and Subictal Neurosis.* In his book Dr. Jonas states that there exists in the brain a continuum extending from the intense focal and generalized electrical discharges seen in grand mal states of epilepsy down to the normally firing brain. Occasionally, for one reason or another, there occur abnormal discharges the symptom manifestations of which may either escape detection or may be quite dramatic and detectable. These symptoms have been given the various names, "ictal events," "subictal events" and "epileptic equivalents." It is further believed that most of the ictal and subictal events or epileptic equivalents are the result of functional or pathological changes in the temporal lobes, the rhinencephalon and the hypothalamus. Ictal and subictal patients may experience an array of rapidly proliferating ideations, emotions and sensations following spontaneous dysrhythmic discharges. Dr. Jonas[1] further states that ictal and subictal phenomena may masquerade as hysteria, anxiety neurosis or *psychopathy.* The ictally-afflicted person expresses an intense anxiety about the ego-alien happenings inside his own mind.

At this point it might be of interest to present a partial list of symptoms which may be the result of ictal and subictal states[1]:

1. Fibrillation or contraction of isolated muscle bundles or groups of muscles, e.g. twitching eyelids, a jumping muscle, an abrupt change in position (such as in nocturnal jactations during light sleep).

2. Paroxysmal or periodic attacks of vertigo, fainting spells, tachycardia, constriction of throat with sensation of suffocation, nausea, vasomotor changes, night sweats, night drooling, headaches, stabbing pains, neuralgia, pins and needles feeling, numbness, loss of feeling, prickly sensations, precordial pains, diarrhea, visual sensations including partial or complete loss of vision, auditory sensations including partial or complete deafness, olfactory and gustatory sensations (namely, a sensation of unpleasant odors and tastes), and the like.

Such terms as *"autonomic seizures," "abdominal migraine,"* and the like, exist in the literature to label the epileptic equivalents resulting from sympathetic and parasympathetic stimulation provoked by an ictal or dysrhythmic discharge. The term *Psychic Seizure* is used to label the following epileptic equivalents: delusion-illusions and hallucinations, micropsia, macropsia, feeling of shapes changing, *deja vu* and *deja entendu,* sudden familiarity and unfamiliarity, a sense of uncanniness, nightmares, somnambulism, fainting, day-dreaming, absent-mindedness, automatism, that is automatic acts followed by amnesia (e.g. a person driving his car for many miles without any memory of doing so), forced thinking, anxiety, depression (often with suicidal thoughts), hysteria, fear, agony, *unexplainable and motiveless behavior, recurrent violent emotional upsets including violent temper tantrums and violent rage. Many authors have variously described these individuals as aggressive, irritable, impulsive, unstable, egocentric, easily offended, obsessive, compulsive, and dependent.*[1]

The symptoms associated with the ictal or subictal events

are widespread—but are rarely if ever diagnosed as such.[1] This is not surprising considering that the list of symptoms enumerated above is only a partial one. Another major reason for the difficulty in diagnosis is that abnormal EEG's may not be demonstrable in many individuals with epileptic equivalents or even with (frank) grand-mal epileptic seizures. The absence of a recognizable neurologic deficit or of an abnormal EEG does not rule out cerebral dysfunction. It only means that methods are not yet available to detect many, if not most, cases of abnormal brain function. The abnormal brain function may be the result of localized encephalitis, excessively high temperatures, hypoxic episodes, metabolic disorders, subdural hematoma, head trauma, genetic influences, and so on. In the aged, the abnormal brain function may be due to postarteriosclerotic degenerative changes. Of special importance to this discussion is the observation that the above-mentioned descriptions of ictally and subictally afflicted individuals resemble very closely the descriptions in the literature of many prison inmates, psychopaths and juvenile delinquents. The following is a very partial list of descriptions in the literature of emotionally disturbed children and juvenile delinquents:

1. "periodically uncontrolled behavior;"
2. "bizarre mannerisms and explosive violence;"
3. "hyperactive, restless, unpredictable, destructive;"
4. "episodic and violent outbursts of impulsive behavior;"
5. "paroxysmal, unbridled aggression, rages and temper tantrums;"
6. "hostility, hypercritical attitudes, pathological lying, feeling of being pushed around, irritability, lack of self-control and pronounced nonconformity;"
7. "hyperreactivity, temper tantrums, fighting, lying, truancy, biting, cruelty to animals, firesetting, sexually acting-out, homicidal and suicidal assaults."

In each of the above cases, the authors felt that there was evidence of cerebral dysrhythmia and that the above symptoms were in fact ictal or subictal events. Several authors have found an extremely high incidence of abnormal EEG's, especially in the fourteen and six positive spikes, in juveniles and adults who committed murder without any apparent motive. Many criminals charged with automotive manslaughter, robbery and murder show evidence of having been in states of altered and clouded consciousness, fugue states, abnormal rages, automatism and destructive behavior. Often there is a partial or complete amnesia to the criminal act. They will rarely attempt to flee or put up resistance when apprehended. They may show no emotions when questioned, thus appearing as hardened and callous criminals.[1] McDonald[2] states that the absence of a motive, premeditation, planning, attempt at concealment and partial or complete loss of memory for the crime is pathognomic for a seizureless epileptic. Thompson[3] states "some sexual psychopaths who engaged in extremely bizarre and socially unacceptable behavior had prominent theta activity in the EEG." Finally, Jonas[1] concludes: *"The guises under which epileptic equivalents masquerade as psychopathic syndromes are many."*

If one accepts the tantalizing hypothesis that many criminals of all ages are actually ictally or subictally afflicted, then they could be included in the general term of minimal brain damage or minimal brain dysfunctions (i.e. MBD), a term universally used to describe a whole host of emotional disturbances. Also, it should be just as logical to include geriatrics suffering from arteriosclerotic brain disease and simple senile degeneration in the waste basket term of brain dysfunction and/or ictal and subictal states. Certainly, one can see a parallelism in many of the symptoms in all of the above-mentioned categories.

I would like now to briefly discuss the actions of several major classes of psychotropic agents on the epileptic equivalents with a twofold goal: (a) the obvious goal of therapy and management, and (b) the responses of the symptoms to the psychotropic drugs as an aid to differential diagnosis in the absence of confirmatory EEG and neurologic signs—as a test of the scheme presented in this paper and so beautifully elaborated in Jonas's[1] book. In order to keep within the time allotted for this discussion, I will only discuss a few of the classes of psychotropic agents—this does not mean that these are the only classes of agents of significance to our discussion.

## A.  THE AMPHETAMINES

In 1937, Bradley[4] introduced the use of Benzedrine Sulfate®
20 (mg/day) in the treatment of children who since infancy
have been irritable, hyperactive and aggressive, with a short
attention span, and whose behavior and mood vary unexplainably
from time to time.  Bradley referred to this as the "organic
reaction type" of behavior.  Phenobarbital, on the other hand,
was shown to be of doubtful value.  Bradley also used Benzedrine
Sulfate parenterally as an emergency sedative in these hyperactive children.  Cutts and Jasper[5] in 1939 noted clinical improvement in seven of twelve children (aged 7 to 10) who were
asocial, hyperactive, impulsive and destructive with Benzedrine
Sulfate (20 mg/day).  Phenobarbital aggravated the symptoms
in nine of the twelve children, while producing no change in
three.  Lindsley and Henry[6] in 1942 noted marked improvement
in thirteen behavior problem children treated with Benzedrine
Sulfate (i.e. hyperactivity, impulsiveness, destructiveness, aggressiveness, distractibility, seclusiveness, sex play, stealing, lying,
etc.).  Phenobarbital, given after Benzedrine improved the
behavior of the children, caused an exacerbation of the symptoms.
Laufer and Denhoff[7] in 1959 state:

> In our experience amphetamine is a specific for the treatment
> of the hyperkinetic syndrome.  A favorable response to amphetamine
> is supportive evidence for a diagnosis of the hyperkinetic syndrome.
> Phenobarbital or other barbiturates are ineffective on the hyper-
> kinetic syndrome.  Instead the great majority of children with this
> syndrome react adversely to such medication.  They often become
> more irritable, unmanageable and active.  This reaction is so marked
> as almost to provide a specific diagnostic test in itself.

Leon Eisenberg and Keith Connors[8] reporting the results of
many studies conclude that stimulants such as dextroamphetamine (Dexedrine®) 10 mg/day and methylphenidate (Ritalin®)
30 mg/day are useful in controlling hyperkinetic and aggressive
behavior disorders in children and adolescents and that phenobarbital can be considerably worse than placebo.  Thus, children
with hyperkinesis or the organic brain syndrome respond para-
doxically to the amphetamines and the barbiturates.  Further
work is needed to determine whether normal children show this

paradoxical effect. This paradoxical effect to the stimulants, however, is found also in certain adults. Hill[9] in 1947 found that amphetamines improved the behavior of psychopaths. He described his subjects as "aggressive" and "bad-tempered." After taking Benzedrine, the subjects' personalities are described as "more integrated" and having a "more mature expression of the primary appetitive drives." J. J. Shovron[10] in 1947 treated three adult psychopaths with Benzedrine. He reported that the patients' aggression lessened as a result of the drug administration. In 1959. Tong[11] treated psychopaths whom he described as "affectionless schizoid" with amphetamine. Also, it has been the clinical impression of our group that many geriatric patients suffering from arteriosclerotic brain disease and simple cerebral degeneration also show a paradoxical effect to the stimulants, such as amphetamine and Ritalin. In addition, Parkinson patients may also show this paradoxical effect to the stimulants.

It is tempting to postulate that the symptoms of hyperkinesis in children, of psychopathy in adults and of irritability and hostility in the agitated geriatric patient are the results of ictal or subictal events and are epileptic equivalents. Thus, one could postulate a decreased threshold of excitation in the effected areas of the brain. That this may be so is indicated by the work of Laufer and Denhoff[7] who demonstrated that children with the hyperkinetic syndrome demonstrate a low threshold for photometrezol activation of the EEG by the technique of Gastaut. They further demonstrated that Dexedrine resulted in a significant raising of the threshold value toward that characteristic of their comparison group. It would be interesting to see if such is the case with adult psychopaths and geriatrics with cerebral degeneration. These authors also postulate that the hyperkinetic syndrome in children may result from injury to or dysfunction of the diencephalon in early life, thus interfering with the normal cortical-diencephalic interplay. These workers, as well as Bradley,[4] suggest that the amphetamines raise synaptic resistance in the diencephalon. It is of interest in this connection to mention that animal data suggest that the amphetamines have anticonvulsant properties. *Thus, we may* *state at this time that the amphetamines and methylphenidate are worthy of further trial in the treatment of juvenile delinquents and adult criminals.* *

In summary, the amphetamines have been shown to be effective in the treatment of MBD in children[4] and in the treatment of aggressive psychopaths.[9, 10] The reasons for this may be as follows: (a) the amphetamines have been shown to possess anticonvulsant properties and (b) the amphetamines are sympathomimetic agents, therefore they are anticholinergic in action. Thus, presumably, they could act as polysynaptic inhibitors in those areas of the CNS where transmission is cholinergic. That this could possibly be a mechanism of action of the amphetamines is strengthened by the observations of many investigators that the antihistamines, such as Benadryl®, have been found effective in the treatment of MBD or hyperkinesis in children.[7] The antihistamines are powerful anticholinergic agents and thus could be expected to inhibit polysynaptic transmission where acetylcholine is the neurotransmitter. The phenothiazines are also very powerful anticholinergic agents. However, their usefulness may be counteracted by their ability to become epileptogenic and also to produce iatrogenic parkinsonism, with an impairment of the extrapyramidal motor system. It is of interest to mention here that both the amphetamines and the antihistamines have a beneficial effect on parkinsonism. Hornykiewicz[12] has shown that in parkinsonism there are lesions in the basal ganglia and substantia nigra, the only areas of the brain known to contain significant amounts of dopamine. Could one consider the paradoxical effects of the sympathomimetic amphetamines in parkinson patients as replacement of dopamine, in organic behavior syndrome in children and in psychopaths as replacement of norepinephrine and epinephrine in the hypothalamus? It is of interest in this connection that Laufer and Denhoff[7] postulate that the hyperkinetic syndrome in children may result from injury to or dysfunction of the diencephalon in early life, thus interfering with the normal cortical-diencephalic interplay.

------

 * See Editor's Note on page 127.

## B. THE ANTICONVULSANTS

Many investigators have found the anticonvulsants, especially diphenylhydantoin (DPH), to be effective in varying degrees in most, if not all, of the ictal and subictal states or epileptic equivalents. Jonas[1] believes that a positive response to DPH might serve as a basis for diagnosing symptoms as being associated with ictal or subictal events. As stated above, the symptoms associated with ictal or subictal events are so widespread that diagnosis is most often very difficult indeed.

The literature on the use of DPH in the treatment of the ictal and subictal events or epileptic equivalents is extremely voluminous and is discussed in depth in Jonas's[1] book. Therefore, I shall confine my remarks here to the use of DPH in the treatment of explosive behavior anomalies in both adults and children.

Diphenylhydantoin has been widely used in the therapy of grand mal and psychomotor epilepsy since 1938. In addition to the control of seizures, DPH was reported to produce improvement in behavior, well-being, cooperation, alertness, general attitude, irritability, temperament and personality of many of the epileptic patients. Recently William J. Turner[13] has reported on the use of Dilantin® in the treatment of nonepileptic neurotics. Dr. Turner states: "Diphenylhydantoin is an effective agent in the relief of symptoms in a variety of neurotic disturbances. It is particularly effective in relief of neurotic depression and *impotent rage,* especially in persons with obsessive or passive-dependent personalities."

McCullagh and Ingram[14] studied a series of patients from their private practice who suffered from migraine-type headaches and emotional disturbances characterized by *Paroxysmal outbursts of hostility or temper tantrums.* The patients ranged from five to forty-eight years of age and included both males and females. Many of the patients were found to have cerebral dysrhythmias, and in some cases a familial tendency for such dysrhythmias was also observed. In one male subject, the outbursts occurred only after the ingestion of alcohol. The EEG, obtained when the patient did not have any alcohol to drink, was well within the normal limits. All of the cases reported were treated successfully with DPH, 100 mg b.i.d. together with 25 mg Thorazine® per day. Jonas[1] cites many references of investigators who demonstrated a frequent incidence of abnormal EEG's in nonepileptic prison inmates, motiveless murders and juvenile delinquents. He further states:

> Many individuals charged with automotive manslaughter, robbery and murder claim that they were under the influence of alcohol at the time of their crimes and that they had no recollection of them. The alcohol seems to have activated seizures of a latent focus in the temporal lobe followed by altered consciousness, fugue states, abnormal rages, automatism and destructive behavior.

In 402 such cases, Marinacci[15] found evidence of temporal lobe seizures, following the ingestion of alcohol, in eighteen patients. Hill and Pond[16] reported a high incidence of abnormal EEG's in persons who committed motiveless murders and who were not under the influence of alcohol at the times the crimes were committed.

During the past thirty years, behavior disorders in children have been extensively studied. The concept of minimal brain damage, delayed cerebral maturation or hyperkinesis encompasses a heterogeneous group of children with a great variety of neurological and/or behavioral disorders. Much work seems to indicate that many of the behavioral symptoms in children may be common to many disorders, regardless of their etiology. Whether there is a known organic etiology or not, one may assume that in some way the child's behavior is the result of a cerebral dysfunction. The absence of a recognizable neurologic deficit or of an abnormal EEG does not rule out cerebral dysfunction. It only means that methods are not yet available to detect many, if not most, cases of abnormal brain function and chemistry. A list of symptoms commonly seen in children with minimal brain damage or hyperkinesis include the following:

1. Overactivity from an early age, often in infancy;
2. Impulsive and uninhibited behavior;
3. Emotional lability with fluctuation of moods;
4. Short attention span with easy distractibility and poor concentration;
5. Unpredictable performance with behavior variability;
6. Inability to delay gratification;

7. Explosiveness and irritability related to low frustration tolerance;
8. Exaggerated response to external stimuli;
9. Specific learning disabilities and erratic school performance;

These symptoms are most frequently seen in children below twelve years of age. They may disappear at any age from eight to eighteen. Many investigators have reported a high incidence of abnormal EEG tracings in nonepileptic emotionally disturbed children and adolescents, especially the fourteen and six per sec positive spike patterns. However, in most instances the changes observed in the EEG's are nonspecific and hence do not by themselves aid in making a diagnosis. Thus, many unrecognized brain disorders, with or without detectable abnormal EEG's, may be the cause of behavior problems both in children and in adults.

Lindsley and Henry[6] in 1942 noted marked improvement in thirteen behavior problem children treated either with Benzedrine sulfate or DPH (i.e. hyperactivity, impulsiveness, destructiveness, aggressiveness, distractibility, seclusiveness, sex play, stealing, lying, etc.). Phenobarbital was ineffective.

Brown and Solomon[17] found in a training school setting that three out of seven boys showed definite improvement on DPH as seen by a reduction in hyperactivity, inattention, less excitability, fewer flare ups of temper and more efficient work patterns. Zimmerman[18] gave DPH to a group of two hundred children having severe behavior disorders. Improvement was seen in 70 percent of the cases. Less excitability, less severe and less frequent temper tantrums, less hyperactivity and distractibility, fewer fears, etc., were some of the behavior changes reported. Putnam and Hood[19] found DPH useful in the treatment of twenty-four juvenile delinquents ranging in age from six to fourteen years of age, with fire setting patterns, disruptive behavior and sexual problems. Chao, Sexton and Davis,[20] Pincus and Glaser,[21] Baldwin and Kenny,[22] Oberst,[23] Rossi,[24] Itil, Rizzo and Shapiro[25], Tec[26], Campbell[27] and Resnick[28] have also demonstrated the beneficial effects of DPH on emotionally disturbed children (MBD) and juvenile delinquents. Resnick[28] also demonstrated the beneficial effects of DPH in both mood and affect in selected, adult male prison inmates. Mark, Sweet, Ervin, Solomon and Geschwind[29] studied patients with focal brain lesions and whose symptoms include: unrestrained and senseless brutality, pathological intoxication, sexual assault, and multiple traffic accidents. The authors have studied over one hundred patients suffering from this "dyscontrol syndrome." Fifteen of these patients had had surgical implantation of the medial temporal lobe with electrodes. The frequent expression of aggressive or assaultive behavior in the interictal period was a most disabling symptom. DPH was found of value in certain of these cases.

From the literature we find ample evidence for the beneficial effects of DPH and other anticonvulsants in neurotics, psychotics, psychopaths[30] and emotionally disturbed children. In some cases, the etiology is known or inferred to be cerebral injury related to trauma or encephalitis, cerebral maldevelopment, delayed cerebral maturation, intense emotional stress, sensory deprivation, cultural deprivation, and the like. In most cases the etiology can neither be determined nor inferred. In some cases there are abnormal EEG patterns; in just as many cases there are no discernible abnormal EEG patterns. Thus DPH seems to affect many heterogeneous groups of patients. However, if these groups of patients are closely examined one finds commonality with respect to certain behavioral characteristics. These are explosiveness, low frustration tolerance, irritability, impulsive behavior, compulsive behavior, aggressive behavior, erratic behavior, inability to delay gratification, mood swings, short attention span, undirected activity, and the like. Perhaps we may postulate that the presence of one or more anatomical or chemical lesions in the brain, from whatever cause, may disorganize the physiology of the remaining intact brain and thus result in a disorganization of synchrony in the firing of the neurones. This may lead to a decreased threshold of excitation with almost continuous firing of the neurones, or it may lead to a spiking pattern of activity resulting in convulsive seizures. Concomitantly, there may result continuous abnormal behavioral changes or abrupt abnormal behavioral changes. That this may be so, in part at least, is indicated by the work of Laufer and Denhoff[7] who demonstrated that children with the hyperkinetic syndrome demonstrate a low threshold for photometrazol activation of the EEG by the technique of Gastaut. Laufer *et al.* also postulate that the hyperkinetic syndrome in children may result from injury to or dysfunction of the diencephalon in early life, thus interfering with the normal cortical-diencephalic interplay.

Since 1938, DPH has been shown to be one of the most effective drugs for the treatment of major motor epilepsy, psychomotor or temporal lobe epilepsy and nonconvulsive epileptic equivalents. DPH has also been shown to be effective in the treatment of cerebral dysrhythmias, without clinical evidence of seizures. DPH has now been demonstrated to be effective in the treatment of behavioral and emotional symptoms concomitant with a wide variety of cerebral dysfunction. The effectiveness of DPH may be due to its ability to decrease the excitability of hyperexcitable cells, in this case, nerve cells. This may result in the reestablishment of normal patterns of brain activity.

Experiments have shown that the aggressive pattern of behavior occurs in almost every case when the hypothalamic area of the brain is damaged. After studying cases of verified lesions of the hypothalamic area, Alpers[31] concluded that the aggressive behavior of his patients had markedly increased. In addition, "obvious antisocial tendencies and partial or complete loss of insight occurred." Fulton and Ingraham[32] made surgical incisions injuring the hypothalamic region of healthy, friendly cats. Immediately after the operation, the cats' behavior changed from playfulness to violent, impulsive sham rage. Patting their backs produced snarling aggressiveness. A similar experiment with dogs, involving removal of the entire thalamic area, brought about a condition of chronic anger.[33] Disease, as well as injury, can cause an increase in antisocial behavior. In 1942, after analyzing a great many postencephalitic children, Bender concluded that the disease increased aggressiveness and decreased the patients' anxiety concerning his uninhibited behavior.[34] Thus, the similarity between the behavior of brain-damaged patients and the sociopath or psychopath may indicate similar cerebral dysfunctions.

Perhaps a biochemical similarity may also be shown to exist. In 1937, Bradley[4] demonstrated the usefulness of the amphetamines in the treatment of the organic behavior syndrome in children. This was considered by many to be a paradoxical effect of the amphetamines. Hill[9] and Shovron[10] reported beneficial, albeit temporary, effects of the amphetamines on aggressive, bad-tempered psychopaths. This could also be considered as a paradoxical effect of the amphetamines. The amphetamines also produce a paradoxical effect in parkinson patients. It is of great interest to the author that in all areas where the paradoxical effects of amphetamines have been observed, DPH also produces beneficial effects.

## C. BENZODIAZEPINES

### I. Chlordiazepoxide (Librium) and Diazepam (Valium®)

These compounds are of interest in this discussion since they are prescribed very extensively for the treatment of the following conditions: tension and anxiety states; somatic complaints which are concomitants of emotional factors; psychoneurotic states manifested by tension, anxiety, apprehension, fatigue, depressive symptoms or agitation; acute agitation, tremor, delerium tremens and hallucinosis due to acute alcohol withdrawal; adjunctively in skeletal muscle spasm due to reflex spasm to local pathology, spasticity caused by upper motor neuron disorders, athetosis, stiff-man syndrome, convulsive disorders, and the like.

These conditions are similar to those which are now being treated very extensively with DPH. There appear to be great similarities in the actions of Librium and Valium on the one hand and DPH on the other—both clinically and on an animal level. Schallek and Kuehn[35] investigated the effects of Librium on the limbic system, which is also referred to as the visceral brain or the rhinencephalon. The limbic system is thought to play a fundamental role in "mood" and "affect." The limbic system is composed of the septum, amygdala and hippocampus. Following electrical stimulation of component parts of the limbic system in decamethonium-immobilized cats, Librium (10 mg/kg iv) inhibited EEG after discharge. Specifically, Librium reduced the duration of after-discharge in the septum and hippocampus and reduced the amplitude of discharge in the amygdala. In freely moving cats with electrodes permanently implanted in the brain, Librium in low doses slowed electrical activity at statistically significant levels only in the hippocampus, amygdala and septum. The cortex was noticeably affected only at higher doses. In addition, naturally vicious laboratory monkeys consistently show aggressive behavior toward their handlers. On Valium, they become quite tame, yet remain alert and coordinated.[36] Kalina[37] has reported excellent success with the use of diazepam (Valium) for the control of the destructive rampages of psychotic criminals. To complete the analogy between DPH and the benzodiazepines (Librium, Valium, Serax®), many reports have appeared indicating the effectiveness of parenteral diazepam (Valium) in the treatment of status epilepticus. Surely, more work is indicated on the use of the benzodiazepines in juvenile delinquents and prisoners.

## D.  PHENOTHIAZINES

Eisenberg[8] and Connors report that "stimulants such as dextroamphetamine and methylphenidate are useful in controlling hyperkinetic (and aggressive) behavior disorders in children and adolescents; that phenothiazines such as prochlorperazine and perphenazine may be no better than placebo; and that phenobarbital can be considerably worse." Jonas[38] has reported that the phenothiazine tranquilizers are contraindicated in the treatment of epileptic equivalents, e.g. the ictal or subictal neuroses. He further states "the administration of tranquilizers to an irritable and impulsive youngster who suffers from epileptic equivalents will only intensify his symptoms." He concludes that the major phenothiazine tranquilizers are contraindicated in cases of cerebral dysrhythmia and in suspected cases of epilepsy, both in children and adults. Furthermore, the phenothiazines may actually precipitate or aggravate an epileptic state or an ictal or subictal neurosis. There is ample evidence in the literature to indicate that phenothiazines are of little value or contraindicated in the treatment of MBD in children, of ictal and subictal states in children and adults and of chronic brain syndrome in geriatric patients. These findings seem to be quite paradoxical when one considers that the phenothiazines are very powerful anticholinergic, antihistaminic and antiserotoningergic agents. The sympathomimetic amines (e.g. the amphetamines) and the antihistamines (e.g. Benadryl®) are also anticholinergic and antihistaminic and yet are beneficial in the treatment of the conditions discussed in this paper. A possible explanation of this paradox would seem to be that the major phenothiazines are epileptogenic, that is, they lower the threshold of excitation and may precipitate or aggravate an epileptic state. Hankoff[39] reported that six patients in a group of fifty-six developed epileptic seizures following promazine treatment. Fabish[49] administered chlorpromazine to epileptics and observed an increase in paroxysmal and hypersynchronous activity in the EEG's. Ingvar and Soderberg[41] produced spindles and slow waves in cats following chlorpromazine, I.V. Since we have assumed that rages, tantrums, acting-out, character problems and all of the epileptic equivalents represent "seizureless epilepsies," certainly agents with "epileptogenic" properties would be contraindicated. On the other hand, a phenothiazine tranquilizer which in clinically effective dosages is usually *not* epileptogenic would be beneficial in the treatment of the conditions discussed in this paper. *As is well known by clinicians, thioridazine (Mellaril®) is such a phenothiazine tranquilizer—effective in children, adults and geriatric patients.*

Kamm and Mandel[42] administered thioridazine to forty-two epileptics with severe ictal manifestations, who had responded poorly to other phenothiazines. He reports that "favorable effect was obtained in thirty-seven patients, nineteen exhibiting marked to moderate improvement. The absence of any increase in seizures constitutes a significant advantage in using thioridazine for the treatment of behavior disorders associated with, or related to, epilepsy."

Another possible explanation for the paradoxical effects of the phenothiazines in the treatment of the ictal and subictal symptoms would seem to be that the phenothiazines can produce extrapyramidal complications. It is of interest in this connection that the incidence of extrapyramidal complications produced by thioridazine is extremely low.

It would seem that drugs capable of raising the threshold of excitation of neurones of the CNS would be of use in the treatment of the aggressive, explosive behavioral anomalies. This, of course, is the mechanism of action of Dilantin. It is well known that the monoamine oxidase inhibitors (i.e. the psychic energizers) also raise the seizure threshold. Thus, more work with this class of agents is indicated. In addition, drugs that are anticholinergic, antihistaminic and antiserotoninergic, but are not epileptogenic, would also be of use in treating the ictal and subictal states. The tricyclic antidepressants, such as imipramine (Tofranil®) would be examples of this. Tofranil has been found to be especially useful for the treatment of enuresis in children with emotional problems.

Another drug which possesses anticholinergic, antihistaminic and antiserotoninergic properties and is not epileptogenic is hydroxyzine (Atarax®, Vistaril®). Hydroxyzine has been found useful in the treatment of the ictal and subictal manifestations, such as tension, anxiety, psychomotor agitation, psychosomatic complaints, behavior problems in children, and the like. Thus, more information on the effects of this drug in aggressive, explosive anomalies is indicated.

### E.   BARBITURATES

As mentioned above, Cutts and Jasper[5] reported that phenobarbital aggravated the symptoms in nine of twelve children who were asocial, hyperactive, impulsive and destructive. Lindsley and Henry[6] reported that phenobarbital, given after benzedrine improved the behavior of emotionally disturbed children, caused an exacerbation of the symptoms. Leon Eisenberg[8] concludes that phenobarbital is considerably worse than placebo in controlling hyperkinetic and aggressive behavior disorders in children and adolescents. It has been the experience of the author that phenobarbital may be contraindicated in the treatment of geriatrics with chronic brain syndrome or simple senile degeneration. The adverse effects of phenobarbital in the treatment of aggressive, explosive behavioral anomalies must surely rank as the most "paradoxical" of all the reactions discussed in this paper. Since phenobarbital is an excellent anticonvulsant, one would expect this drug to produce beneficial effects in the aggressive, explosive anomalies, as well as in the ictal and subictal symptomatology. A possible explanation might be the concept, held by many investigators, that places the primary site of action of the barbiturates at the diencephalic rather than the cortical level. We have already mentioned that Laufer and Denhoff[7] postulate that the hyperkinetic syndrome in children may result from injury to or dysfunction of the diencephalon in early life, thus interfering with the normal cortical-diencephalic interplay. Should the barbiturates depress the diencephalon more than the cortex, then the normal cortical-diencephalic interplay should be interfered with, thus actually producing a cerebral dysrhythmia with concomitant behavioral manifestations. Certainly much more work is indicated in this area.

---

*Editor's note*: The chemical control of sex offenders, sudden violence and, also, a precedent setting case of an acquittal in a multiple homicide (Wyoming vs. Payne) have occurred since this presentation. Our traditional "characterological" view of morality seems to be giving way to a "chemical" view. The surgical implantation of long-acting drugs encased in a semi-permiable plastic also is now under study for male sex offenders and micro-implants in specific brain areas to control anger also have been successfully used.

## REFERENCES

1. Jonas, A. D.: *Ictal and Subictal Neurosis, Diagnosis and Treatment.* Springfield, Thomas, 1965.
2. McDonald, J. M.: *Psychiatry and the Criminal.* Springfield, Thomas, 1958.
3. Thompson, G. N.: Relationship of sexual psychopathy to psychomotor epilepsy and its variants. *J Nerv Ment Dis, 121*:374, 1955.
4. Bradley, C.: The behavior of children receiving benzedrine. *Amer J Psychiat, 94*:577, 1937.
5. Cutts, K. K., and Jasper, H. H.: Effect of benzedrine sulfate and phenobarbital on behavior problems of children with abnormal EEG. *Arch Neurol Psychiat, 41*:1138, 1939.
6. Lindsley, D. B., and Henry, C. E.: The effect of drugs on behavior and the electroencephalograms of children with behavior disorders. *Psychosom Med, 4*:140, 1942.

7. Laufer, M. W., and Denhoff, E.: Hyperkinetic behavior syndrome in children. *J Pediat, 50*:463, 1957.

8. Eisenberg, L.: Behavioral manifestations of cerebral damage in childhood. In Birch, H. G. (Ed.): *Brain Damage in Children.* Baltimore, Williams and Wilkins, 1964.

9. Hill, D.: Amphetamine in psychopathic states. *Brit J Addict, 44*:50, 1947.

10. Shovron, J. J.: Benzedrine in psychopathy and behavior disorders. *Brit J Addict, 44*:58, 1947.

11. Tong, J.: Stress Reactivity in Relation to Delinquent and Psychopathic Behavior. 1959. Cited by Craft, M.: In Psychopathic personalities: A review of diagnosis, etiology, prognosis and treatment. *Brit J Crimin, I (No. 3)*: January 1961.

12. Hornykiewicz, O.: The occurrence of dopamine (3-hydroxytyramine) in the central nervous system: Its relationship to Parkinsonism. *German Med Monthly, 7*:344, 1962.

13. Turner, W. J.: The usefulness of diphenylhydantoin in treatment of non-epileptic emotional disorders. *Int J Neuropsychiat, 3 (Suppl. 2)*: 58, 1967.

14. McCullagh, W. H., and Ingram, W., Jr.: Headaches and hot tempers. *Dis Nerv Syst, 17(9)*:279, 1956.

15. Marinacci, A. A.: Special type of temporal lobe seizure following ingestion of alcohol. *Bull Los Angeles Neurol Soc, 28*:241, 1963.

16. Hill, D., and Pond, D. A.: Reflections on 100 capital cases submitted to EEG. *J Ment Sci, 98*:23, 1952.

17. Brown, W. T., and Solomon, C. I.: Delinquency and the electro-encephalograph. *Amer J Psychiat, 98*:499, 1942.

18. Zimmerman, F. T.: Explosive behavior anomalies in children on an epileptic basis. *New York J Med, 56*:2537, 1956.

19. Putnam, T. J., and Hood, O. E.: Project Illinois: A study of therapy in juvenile behavior problems. *Western Med* :231, July 1964.

20. Chao, D.; Sexton, J. A., and Davis, S. D.: Convulsive equivalent syndrome of childhood. *J Pediat, 64*:499, 1964.

21. Pincus, J. H., and Glaser, G. H.: The syndrome of minimal brain damage in childhood. *New Eng J Med, 275*:27, 1966.

22. Baldwin, R., and Kenny, T. J.: Learning disabilities. In Hellmuth, J. (Ed.): *Learning Disabilities.* 1966, vol. 2, p. 313.

23. Oberst, B. B.: Preventive care of infants and children. *J Lancet, 86*:331, 1966.

24. Rossi, A. O.: Psychoneurologically impaired child. *New York J Med, 67*:902, 1967.

25. Itil, T. M.; Rizzo, A. E., and Shapiro, D. M.: Study of behavior and EEG correlation during treatment of disturbed children. *Dis Nerv Syst, 28*:731, 1967.

26. Tec, L.: Efficacy of diphenylhydantoin in childhood psychiatric disorders. *Amer J Psychiat, 124*:156, 1968.
27. Campbell, E. W., Jr., and Young, J. D., Jr.: Enuresis and its relationship to electroencephalographic disturbances. *J Urol, 96*:947, 1966.
28. Resnick, O.: The psychoactive properties of diphenylhydantoin: Experiences with prisoners and juvenile delinquents. *Int J Neuropsychiat, 3 (Suppl. 2)*:530, 1967.
29. Personal communication.
30. Silverman, D.: The electroencephalograph and therapy of criminal psychopaths. *J Crimin Psychopathol, 5(3)*:439, 1944.
31. Alpers, B.: Hypothalamic destruction. *Psychosom Med, 2*:286, 1944.
32. Fulton, J. F., and Ingraham, F. D.: Emotional disturbances following experimental lesions of the base of the brain. *J Physiol, 90*:353, 1929.
33. East, W. N.: Psychopathic personality and crime. *J Ment Sci, 91*:426, 1945.
34. Bender, L.: Postencephalitic behavior disorders in childhood. In Neal, Josephine B.: Encephalitis. New York, Grune and Stratton, 1942.
35. Schallek, W., and Kuehn, A.: Effects of psychotropic drugs on limbic system of cat. *Proc Soc Exp Biol Med, 105*:115, 1960.
36. Randall, L. O.; Schallek, W.; Heise, G. A.; Keith, E. F., and Bagdon, R. E.: The psychosedative properties of methaminodiazepoxide. *J Pharmacol Exp Ther, 120*:163, 1960.
37. Kalina, R. K.: Use of Diazepam in the violent psychotic patient: A preliminary report. *Colorado GP, 4*:11, 1962.
38. Jonas, A.: The emergence of epileptic equivalents in the era of tranquilizers. *Int J Neuropsychiat, 3*:40, 1967.
39. Hankoff, I. D.: Convulsions complicating ataractic therapy. *New York Med J, 57*:2967, 1957.
40. Fabish, W.: The effect of chlorpromazine on the EEG of epileptics. *J Neurol Neurosurg Psychiat, 20*:185, 1957.
41. Ingvar, D. H., and Soderberg, U.: Effects of chlorpromazine on cerebral circulation and EEG in cats. *Arch Neurol Psychiat, 78*:254, 1957.
42. Kamm, I., and Mandel, A.: Thioridazine in the treatment of behavior disorders in epileptics. *Dis Nerv Syst, 28*:46, 1967.

## EDITOR'S NOTE

In April, 1971 a special commission of the AMA confirmed the dramatically beneficial effect of amphetamines on some types of hyperkinetic children. Great care in diagnosis and continuing observation by a trained psychiatrist must accompany this treatment.

# 9

## PANEL ON DRUGS AND SOCIETY IN THE YEAR 2000

### NATHAN S. KLINE—CHAIRMAN

THE PANEL MEMBERS, each allowed a fifteen minute opening statement, included (in order of presentation): Arthur Koestler, author of numerous books, among them *Darkness at Noon, The Act of Creation,* and most recently *The Ghost in the Machine;* Ashley Montagu, anthropologist, author and lecturer; Judge John Oliver, Judge of the Fifth Circuit Court, St. Louis; John Campbell, science fiction writer and editor of *Analog Science Fiction,* and Nathan S. Kline, clinician and researcher. Free discussion followed the opening statements.

\* \* \* \*

*Mr. Koestler:* In a recent book\* I advanced a very unpopular hypothesis. It says, in a nutshell, that the sorry state of affairs reflected in the daily newspapers is not just transitory, that there is in the native equipment of our species a built-in engineering error, a construction fault, which accounts for the paranoic streak running through our absurd and tortured history. Already at its bloody, prehistoric dawn we find the ubiquitous practice of human sacrifice to which anthropologists have paid much too little attention, although it can be traced to every culture on the globe. It is the first symptom of that more or less controlled schizophrenia which, in a variety of changing forms, has accompanied us to this day.

When Swift's Gulliver got to Lilliput, he learnt to his surprise that for a number of generations wars had been waged to decide whether a boiled egg should be opened at the broad end or at

---

\* *The Ghost in the Machine.* New York, Macmillan, 1968.

the pointed end. That seems funny, but if you remember that, for several weeks now, negotiations have been going on in Paris to decide whether the Vietnam negotiators should sit at a round table or a rectangular table or a square table while people are dying out there in rains of napalm, you will perhaps admit that reality is not very far from the satirist's invention.

Let me mention a few of the main symptoms of the paranoic streak in the species man. The first is, of course, intraspecies killing and intraspecies warfare. We are told by the ethnologists that with two exceptions—rats and a few species of ants—fighting within the species is a ritualized affair which stops short of actual killing. Needless to remind you that the predator and the prey always belong to different species. In our own species, however, there are no built-in inhibitions against the killing of nonspecifics. Furthermore, man engages not only in individual homicide, which is of little importance in history, but in organized intraspecific warfare. It is the most outstanding characteristic of our species and now threatens it with total extinction.

How did this biologically unique predicament arise? The generally accepted answer is that it arose because man is an aggressive creature. The basic point which I want to emphasize is that individual aggression committed for selfish motives—robbery, rape and murder—plays a quite insignificant part in history. *Our tragic history is not caused by too much selfishness or too much aggression, but by too much altruism and unselfish devotion to tribe, nation, totem, flag, leader, church, party, or ideology.* To put it pointedly, we are suffering not from an excess of aggression but from an excess of love—misplaced, misguided infatuation with flags, slogans, belief-systems. I think such a diagnosis does open the possibility of a positive therapeutic approach, because I think it certainly won't be, within, say, twenty-five years, beyond the reach of psychopharmacology to immunize a person against morbid infatuation with a Circe— or with a Hitler.

How did this pathogenic disposition arise? I would like to mention five possible causative factors. The first is the protracted helplessness and dependence of the human neonate, which seems to be at the root of the transference situation, with its implications for the ready acceptance of the authority of father, leader, dogmatic beliefs.

The second factor is more speculative: when our primate ancestors emerged from the forests into the plains and took to hunting prey which was bigger and faster than themselves they became perilously dependent on solidarity and mutual aid, out of which developed tribal cohesion, esprit de corps, nationalism, and so on.

My third point is the emergence of language. Language facilitates communication within the group, but at the same time erects barriers between groups. Think of Canada, Belgium, the fighting between Maharatis and Gujuratis in India. But the perils of language go further than that. I am sure you have seen results of field studies on Japanese monkeys which have shown that different groups of monkeys are capable of developing different "cultures," different habits or fashions. Some groups wash their bananas in the river before eating them, others don't. Sometimes migrating groups of banana-washers meet nonwashers, and the two groups watch each other's strange behavior with apparent surprise. But they do not follow the example of the Lilliputians and go to war, and I think the main reason why they don't go to war is that they have got no language which would enable them to crystallize their respective habits into articulate slogans, manifestoes, ideologies. Slogans and credos have an explosive power. Without language there could be no poetry, but there could also be no war, because ultimately, as some Frenchman said, wars are waged for words.

My fourth causative factor is awareness of death. Man is the only animal that knows about death, and this is an indigestible knowledge which has to be rationalized by filling the atmosphere with demons, the ghosts of departed ancestors, and deities which may occasionally be benevolent, but mostly are capricious, malicious, and have to be constantly appeased and cajoled—hence the ubiquitous practice of human sacrifice in the wake of the discovery of death.

This leads to my fifth point, which is the split between irrational, affected-based beliefs and rational thinking. May I remind you of Alice's innocent remark in *Alice in Wonderland*, "But this is impossible," to which the Red Queen answers: "But I always believe in six impossible things before breakfast." That's our tragedy. There seems to be an icebox built somewhere into our skulls which is the seat of cold logic and rational thought, and next to it there is a hothouse of irrational, affect-based beliefs. But the two do not interact, there is no integration. Instead of integration, there is a kind of chronic, schizophrenic split, on the psychological level, between emotion and reason, faith and logic, and underlying it on the physiological level, a "schizophysiology."

The term was coined by Paul MacLean of the NIMH, who developed the Papez-MacLean theory of emotions. It suggests that in the last stages of our evolution, the neocortex developed at such a rapid and explosive rate that it never became completely integrated with the phylogenetically older parts of the brain. The result seems to be inadequate coordination or insufficient feedbacks between the modern brain, as the seat of language, of rational and abstract thought on the one hand, and the archaic parts which mediate emotional behavior. I know that Delgado and some of his colleagues disagree with the Papez-MacLean theory, but I nevertheless feel strongly attracted by it, and have included it into the proposed causative factors of the human predicament because it provides a very plausible evolutionary explanation of what has gone wrong with our species. And if this diagnosis of the predicament is correct, then there is some hope that neuropsychopharmacology might find an answer to it.

❊    ❊    ❊    ❊

*Dr. Montagu*: It has been known for many years that agents such as mustard gas, colchicine, radioactive isotopes, and so forth are capable of altering the structure of chromosomes. Today, we have good evidence that there are many substances capable of damaging human chromosomes and, at least in experimental animals, resulting in defective offspring. The question I shall discuss here is, whether, in the future, it will be possible by means of various agents, particularly drugs, to alter chromosome structure in man. This is a highly important question in view of the great and humanly dangerous powers such possible knowledge could place in the hands of the wrong people.

So, it seems to me that it is not so much foreknowledge of these dangerous possibilities upon which we should concentrate, but, rather, upon the manner in which we could prevent the development of the wrong people. For, no matter what safeguards we institute against the misuse of knowledge, so long as there are wrong people in positions of power there will always remain the possibility that such people will manage to circumvent any proposed safeguards. The only practical safeguard against wrong people is to prevent their development. By this I do not mean nipping them in the bud as embryos or fetuses, although in some cases involving the development of predictable disorders and/or malformations this is already being done.

What I mean is the institution of an educational system. I deliberately hesitate to say a socialization process because that, to some people, sounds almost as evil as suggesting that boys and girls ought to matriculate before being admitted to higher institutions of learning, and every good American knows that Socialism is the back door to Communism. But, not being intimidated by words or their perverters, I shall continue to use the words "the socialization process" to mean that process by which the child is turned into a humane being according to the requirements of the culture in which he is conditioned.

*In brief, what we stand most in need of is not more knowledge, but more sound use of what we already know concerning the making of humane beings.* What this implies, what I mean by a good, humane being, is one who has been helped to realize that his evolutionary potentialities for being a lover, not only of his fellow man, but of the whole world of animate and inanimate nature, are the necessary and sufficient conditions for development as a humane being.

Now, what do I mean by a lover? By love, I mean from a sociobiological point of view, and from no other point of view but that, behavior that confers survival benefits upon others in a creatively enlarging manner, in plain English, behavior that not only enables the other to survive, but to grow and develop in a more fully fulfilled manner than he otherwise would. *This is the formula for love: the conferral of survival benefits upon the other in a creatively enlarging manner.* This is what we need to teach at home and this is what education should be all about— not the three R's as primary, but love as primary and the three R's as secondary techniques and skills in the service of the greater realization of one's potentialities for development as a good humane being. Love, and goodness have far greater adaptive value for the human species than any other forms of behavior. Evil is a disoperative form of behavior that individuals who have been frustrated in their need for love use as a substitute for love. Power becomes the means by which they seek to fill the vacuum that has been left within them as the result of the lack-love experience of their early years, and, of course, they do not know how to use power in a loving but only in a frustrated, a deformed, and insecure manner. They abuse it and produce disaster all about them.

It is this kind of deformed individual, deformed by a socialization process which is based on a confusion of unsound values, who can be, I believe, prevented from ever developing by a socialization process which is firmly based on a value system founded, not on success in terms of external validations, but on the discipline and value of love. What this implies is a complete revaluation of our value system—a value system which constitutes the basis of our socialization and educational system. Unless we make this revaluation, I foresee that the end of the human species is very likely to occur in a relatively short time.

From the immediately practical point, the number one problem that must be solved, as we are simultaneously working on the solution of the many other social problems which at least require amelioration, is the population problem.

Unless we solve that problem, we shall succeed in solving no other.

And, now, let us take off into the great blue yonder and assume a warless world of the future where all, or virtually all, are flourishingly healthy, that is, able to love and able to work. What can we envisage as the developments in neuropsychopharmacology in relation to man's genetic constitution and its future evolution? To begin with, let it be said that there is now plenty of evidence that the evolution of genetic systems occurred mainly by chromosomal duplication, by duplication in normal chromosomal numbers in man, whether *euploid or aneuploid or polyploid* or in the form of mosaics or otherwise, and all these conditions are almost always associated with deficiency or maldevelopment of some sort. Drugs, therefore, capable of producing such chromosomal abnormalities are clearly to be avoided.

What kinds of drugs then are to be considered in relation to the genetic evolution of man? To that question I would firmly reply NONE should be considered. For the time being, and for a durable period to come, man must be considered to have evolved genetically far enough. Some would have it that he has already evolved too far and if he goes on much further he will evolve himself out of existence. So I believe it would be highly undesirable to attempt to influence his evolution by playing tricks with his genetic constitution.

But, what we can look forward to is a continuing development and sophistication of drugs which activate genes, which, owing to the failure or absence of one or more amino acid, have resulted in some developmental defect. The failure, as is well known, of one valine unit is sufficient to result in sickle cell anemia. There are a great many similar genetic conditions.

Through reconstitution of the missing or defective units, the repair of such deficiencies, rather than their alleviation, may safely be predicted as a form of genetic therapy or engineering which the future will, undoubtedly, see developed. At the rate of present genetic discovery, it would be folly to predict when such developments may become realities.

The statements made by some authorities that such advances will take several hundred years may turn out to be rather conservative. Such advances will prove to be a boon to humanity and considerably reduce the quantum of suffering in the world.

However, advances which are already being made in related areas may make such genetic therapy, largely, if not wholly, unnecessary. For example, by para-abdominal amniocentesis it is now possible to withdraw some of the amniotic fluid and examine the desquamated cells of the fetus and, by karyotyping them, it is possible to pick up anomalous chromosomal conditions of which, today, several hundred are already known and recognized.

With such information at our disposal it becomes possible to determine whether a malformed or otherwise deficient child will result, and whether or not the pregnancy should be terminated or whatever else may be necessary to meet the conditions presented.

By the use of such methods, we may again foresee an enormous reduction in the number of malformed and otherwise defective children born to future generations. Here our predictions can be very much more secure than for the advent of chromosomal reconstitution, for the process has already begun and major advances in this direction are a matter of the immediate future.

While, then, we may expect to see in the future, as a result of the application of such methods, a sizeable reduction in the number of defective persons owing to the inherent variability of the genetic system and the operation of a great many other factors of endogenous and exogenous origin, such as aging effects, paternal and maternal dysfunction, cosmic and background radiation, and the like, there will always continue to be a large number of fetuses that will suffer defective development. Here prenatal and genetic diagnosis will always continue to be necessary.

And now for the possibilities of that *Brave New World* which Aldous Huxley so brilliantly envisaged in his book of that title many years ago.

Will it be possible to alter genetic structure in such a measure that governments, whether of dictators or otherwise, will be able to produce the citizens they want like the Queen, drones, workers, and soldiers of insect colonies? Is the insectification of man a genuine possibility? The answer is that it unequivocally is. The fixation of traits the insects have achieved in the normal course of evolution and genetic change, man is capable of bringing about by artificial manipulation. Unfortunately, this is the kind of knowledge that is likely to be acquired in the ordinary course of research on the manipulation of the genetic system for neutral or beneficial ends.

It seems to me, therefore, that the only protection against the misuse of such knowledge is a moral or ethical one, namely, the resolution of all workers and their representative groups who may in any way be involved in such investigation to make themselves positively responsible for the use to which their discoveries are put. The logistics of this will, of course, have to be worked out by the individuals and scientific bodies most closely involved in the relevant facts.

To conclude, it is none too early to begin the consideration of the general and ethical principles which should apply and be operative in the pursuit of all scientific research and its possible practical uses. Man has eaten of the tree of the knowledge of Good and Evil and is, with few exceptions, no longer able to distinguish between the one and the other, and has for long worshipped evil as if it were his good. The God of the common man's idolatry, and often of his own, has become the scientist—a God with clay feet, who stands very much in need of protection for his own *hubris*.

Until recently all medical men, upon graduation, were required to take the Hippocratic Oath. It is, in my view, vastly more important that all scientists take an oath recognizing and avowing their responsibility to their fellow man for the work they will and will not engage in and for the prevention of any possible or contemplated harmful application to which their work may be put. Every scientific society should have a code of ethics, to which each of its members should be required to subscribe, specifically directed toward the control of scientific research and its practical applications.

I would respectfully suggest that this College might well begin by setting the example to others by drawing up such a code before these meetings are terminated. Such a code can only be drawn up after much thought and critical evaluation.* Clearly, research that can lead to results that will greatly benefit mankind may also often be used for the opposite purpose. It will be necessary to develop some system of control against the

---

* See Editor's Note number 1 on page 158.

misuse of such knowledge. The development of such agents as poison gases is clearly directed to one end, and here the resolve of the scientist should be in no doubt. He should have nothing whatever to do with the research leading to the development of such murderous agents. Any scientist who engages in such work should be drummed out of the community of scientists and his employers boycotted until they have reformed. The scientist can no longer with handwashing indifference engage in pursuits in the name of science without the fullest subscription to the central purpose from which scientific endeavor should never depart, the welfare of man. Because the scientist, directly or indirectly, is involved in tampering with nature and its control, his responsibility is that indeed of a God in whose power lie no less than the decisions of life and death and virtually everything in between; his responsibilities to mankind, indeed to the whole nature, animate and inanimate, are far greater than those of any other kind of man. No one should ever enter the field of science without full recognition of that fact.

*     *     *     *

*Judge Oliver*: What, if any, wisdom our culture will exercise concerning both old and new drugs is subject to the primary question of whether we can make an exception to the apparent principle that history teaches—that we learn nothing from history.

When I was in college during the era of alcohol prohibition I had a roommate who spent a good deal of time trying to get a poster that had been published by the antisaloon league in 1913. That poster suggested:

1. Alcohol inflames the patient, thus making the temptations in sex-sin unusually strong.
2. Alcohol decreases the power of control thus making the resisting of sex temptation especially difficult.

He wanted to draw a red line through the message of the poster: "Avoid All Alcoholic Drink Absolutely. The Control of Sex Impulses Will Be Easy and Disease, Dishonor, Disgrace and Degradation Will Be Avoided."

I think we all must recognize that John Stuart Mill's suggestion, approximately one hundred years ago, has not been accepted by any society that possesses many attributes of complexity. Mills, as you recall, in his "Essay on Liberty" suggested the very simple principle that the sole end for which mankind is warranted, individually or collectively, in interfering with the liberty of action of any of its number is self-protection. He continued, "no member of a civilized society can rightfully be compelled to do or forbear because it will be better for him to do so, because it will make him happier, because, in the opinion of others, to do so would be wise or even right."

Our obvious failures, in the past, to coerce virtue by legislation in regard to alcohol did not deter a new attempt to coerce what people call virtue in regard to other drugs.* The problems, of course, are different because different drugs are involved. I think it is appropriate to direct attention to the statement of the Director of the Bureau of Prisons, who had more firsthand experience with the operation of our present narcotic laws than any other person. Speaking at the 1958 symposium of the History of Narcotic Drug Addiction Problems at the National Institute of Mental Health at Bethesda, the distinguished criminologist, James V. Bennett, then Director of the Bureau, stated:

> My own view is that the problem of narcotic addiction must ultimately and properly be defined as a health problem, not as a problem of morals, or a problem of crime. The past twenty-five years have, I feel, demonstrated amply that neither the punitive approach nor hospitalization alone provides the answer. In the final analysis, the responsibility is the community's. To provide continuous and long-term care for the addict is not significantly different, in my opinion, from that which it owes, not only to the alcoholic, the person whose mental illness is in remission, and who no longer requires hospitalization, or any other physically or emotionally handicapped citizen.
>
> A practical solution to the most difficult problem cannot be based on action based on fear or motivated by vengeance.

Anslinger, however, tells us in his book, *The Murderers*, that in 1937 the Bureau of Narcotics had temporarily lost its campaign to place marijuana, a then new drug, under federal control. We, to use his own words, "continued to hammer at the facts" to get Congress to act.

---

* See Editor's Note number 2 on page 158.

Scientists, I believe, must come to recognize that the "facts" upon which legislative action is taken, are extremely hard things to come by. I sometimes am consoled when contemplating the apparent wickedness of man to think of the statement of Marcus Aurelius, some 2000 years back, who suggested that we think on this doctrine "that reasoning beings are created one for another's sake, that to be patient is a branch of justice and that men often do wrong without really intending it."

That quote, of course, is introductory to the only suggestion that I can make in regard to what our culture may be in the year 2000. I offer it in the spirit of the great Jefferson who suggested that it's better to light a candle than curse the darkness.

The thought is not a new one. Mr. Justice Holmes suggested as long ago as 1891 that the business of lawyers was to make plainer the way from something to the whole thing. If the subject is law, the roads to anthropology, the science of man, the theory of legislation and ethics are among the several paths that must be followed to one's final view of life. He emphasized that to be master of any branch of knowledge, one must master those which lie next to it.

This is not the time or place to trace Mr. Justice Cardoza's appeal for a Ministry of Justice, served by medical knowledge, outlined in his 1928 address to the New York Academy of Medicine, or to discuss the great Dean Pound's efforts to implement that idea. Professor Sheldon Glueck traced that history in his 1963 proposal for interdisciplinary institutes to be located on the campuses of leading universities throughout the country.

It is, however, important to take note of Professor Harry Calvin's statement that a remarkable step has been taken recently in regard to the relationship between law and science particularly in the last ten years. Social scientists are now included as full-time members of many law school faculties. Ten law teachers have been included in the group of scientists that gathered at the Palo Alto Center for the Advanced Study of the Behavioral Sciences. The American Bar Foundation and the Walter Mark Institute annually sponsor interdisciplinary research. The joint work of the American Bar Foundation and, of all people, the American Medical Association, made one of the great contributions towards sanity in the extremely complicated area of the law and marijuana.*

Calvin suggested, in a recent paper, that his experience made apparent that the basic question of the role that science must play is in forming public opinion on matters which must be governed by law. Interestingly enough, he used a drug to illustrate his point. *Science must learn that it cannot have a meaningful impact on the living law until it learns that its specialized knowledge must first become a part of the popular learning.* When that happens, but only if that happens, can science expect to enter law via the normal process under which every other piece of legislation is enacted. Until scientific knowledge becomes more widely shared, it cannot expect to have appropriate impact on the law. Until the public generally accepts the view that there are in fact scientific differences between marijuana and heroin, an example used by Calvin, the science of the matter is not likely to make much difference in what laws may be enacted.

The scientific community is an apparent world unto itself, but it is also a part of a larger world in which all mankind lives. The authorization of a federal judicial center by the last Congress created, for the first time in American history, a research oriented organism and institution for the Federal Judiciary. The day is not far distant when the research director of that Institute is going to be searching for scientists who know the scientific facts, not only about drugs, but about all forms of human behavior. That center may want to know what group of scientists are willing to become a part of an interdisciplinary team to study what should and what should not be done about the new drugs that will be discovered between now and the year 2000, indeed to study what should and what should not be done about things we already know. I am personally convinced that if data more reliable than that upon which the Congress acted in regard to alcohol is not effectively made available to the public learning, that our legislation concerning drugs, both known and unknown, will make the year 2000 a rather unhappy place.

_____

* See Editor's Note number 3 on page 158.

On the other hand, I am sufficiently a congenital optimist and I live in the hope that either the College or some of its members will create a chair or a division to establish liaison with people who are walking down different paths which lead to a common end.

*    *    *    *

*Mr. Campbell*: There is necessarily in any discussion of what should be done and what can be done the requirement that we determine what *is* and what *can be*. Basically, this is equivalent to the remark of the psychiatrist's patient, "Doctor, I'll face reality, if you'll define exactly what that is!"

Most men tend to be pretty sure they know what reality is— "what the score is"—and are usually annoyed, disturbed or angered if someone questions the established beliefs by which they live.

Science fiction lives in a sort of half-world—like fables, science fiction is neither "true" nor "false," for a story may be philosophically true and factually false at the same time. For example, I doubt that there ever was a particular Samaritan who did precisely as Jesus described in His parable, thus the Parable of the Good Samaritan must be labelled "factually false" —although it expresses a philosophical truth.

Science fiction permits us to explore other possible realities, other possible cultural concepts, and, as such, is anything but a new form of literature. Plato's *Republic* was a form of science fiction, all the Utopian novels were. Because it can remove us from the immediate-us-here-now into some pseudoimaginary situation, we can discuss openly problems that are too controversial for open discussion otherwise—as Dean Swift realized when he wrote his science fiction stories of *Gulliver's Travels*.

True, Dean Swift didn't use spaceships to reach distant planets; in his day, the Earth was poorly explored and he could use shipwreck on distant islands to the same effect. But, his strange aliens on those remote worlds could be super-giants or microminiaturized or very horsey; the essence is the same. It's a way of looking at reality through different eyes—and possibly understanding better what we see through our own.

There are several basic arguments here with which I wish to quarrel. Fundamentally, there is a great confusion between ethics and tribal mores. By my own definition, ethics are the laws of the universe which men try to express and call mores. Newton's law of gravity is not *the* Law of Gravity. Einstein added corrections. We need more corrections, but there is a Law of Gravity in the universe.

Similarly, our tribal mores are not the laws of ethics, but I believe that in the universe there are laws that can eventually be discovered. Tribal mores are a culture's best effort at expressing the laws that really exist.

Now, the only way I can define "good" in terms that will rise above the local tribal mores is say that "good" is "that which works in hundred-million-year terms." If it works in the long run, it's a good idea. Evolution is made up of good ideas—the ones that work.

Evolutionary forces work in ways that are by no means pleasant. Evolutionary forces work to the benefit of the species, not in the interests of the individual. In the same way, you as an organism seek to promote your own survival even if it requires the destruction or loss of the member. If you've got to save a life, you will lose a finger. A species basically is interested in species survival. Its ethics, therefore, is not always the individual's concept of good.

One of our problems is to distinguish between "hurt" and "injure." The problem of definitions is extremely important, and people don't like it because it isn't always pleasant. The best way I have been able to define the difference between hurt and injure and to communicate it is simply to say that dentistry hurts but doesn't injure, while morphine never hurts but does injure. That which is hurtful merely causes pain, but pain is not necessarily injurious. The usual code of mores is simply a tribal taboo, a system of rituals and taboos. It may or may not be good. One of the reasons why we never learn from history comes down basically to the fact that history is always written by the winners, and it, therefore, shows that "it all happened for the best." This is inevitable because only the winners live to write it—and the result was the best for them!

Consider this proposition. Suppose we do have a means of controlling the DNA, RNA genetic potentials of individuals.

Suppose once, a million years ago, there was a great congress of gorillas who assembled for the purpose of determining the best methods of eugenically breeding a super-gorilla—a really superior gorilla. Their ideal would probable have bigger muscles, stronger teeth—they wouldn't wind up with the concept of a mangy individual who had lost all his hair, whose jaw was shrunken, whose head was bloated. This is not what they would consider a desirable form.

Now we must recognize that human evolution does not stop here. We are not the end product of evolution; we are merely the product *so far*. Make no mistake, we have a long way to go, and it involves evolution, and we feel perfectly right in saying that man will evolve himself out of existence. He will. The reptiles evolved themselves out of existence too. The successful ones did—they are called mammals now.

The newer forms of life that are to come are not something that we today can predict. I do not want too much tribal taboo, regulation. Once upon a time it was very easy for a man to define precisely what evil was. Evil was change. Change was evil. Violation of the tribal taboos—that was evil. The individuals who did violate tribal taboos proved that violating the taboos was always bad luck. They always died. The tribes saw to it, and that proved that it was bad luck to violate the taboos. It was a real-life circular argument, or self-fulfilling prophecy, but it stopped anyone with disturbing new ideas. However, some original thinkers escaped and they became barbarians. This was terrible for the tribes, but it was actually a step forward— a greater freedom of development. We don't like barbarians now but that's simply because we've gone still another step beyond.

Remember, the barbarian considers that the man who works for a living is a slave. He has no manhood. He's no man. No true barbarian will work for a living. That's why our ancestors who came over to this country and were faced with a great deal of work to be done and not enough people to do the work imported slaves from Africa, but did not enslave the local natives. It couldn't be done. The Africans were still in a ritual taboo type of culture, but the local Indians were in a barbarian culture and a barbarian will not work for a living. He'll die fighting, and the Indians did. The early settlers never were able to enslave Indians.

The next step up is what we call the citizen who will work for a living. Now we do not know what the next step is—but you can positively guarantee you'll hate it when it comes along.

One of the things we can do in science fiction is to try to look at some of the possibiilties. That's what we've been doing.

I would like to make one comment on the use of drugs. Are we to believe that a system of such enormously complex balances as is represented by an intelligent living species will be improved by making some simple changes? I believe that it is extremely improbable.

Hallucinogens do not improve mentation. They have been tried by a number of different cultures over many centuries. No culture that accepted hallucinogens widely has ever demonstrated high creativity. Western culture, as we know it, has throughout its history had a strong resistance to hallucinogenics of any kind. Laws haven't been enacted against them particularly. Social disapproval has been quite effective, and it is Western culture that has generated more creative concepts than any culture anywhere that has ever used hallucinogenic drugs. That's my reason for saying that hallucinogenic drugs are evil. They didn't work.

*   *   *   *

*Dr. Kline*: As a working scientist, my concern is in pursuing whatever we call truth wherever it may lead. At the same time, I am a citizen of a culture and, as such, have some voice in the way research and science is directed. I was involved in the creation of psychopharmacology and more specifically in what is now the Psychopharmacology Service Branch of the National Institute of Mental Health. By giving Congressional testimony as to the need for research in this area I was able, acting as a citizen, to have something to say about the direction in which science would proceed. I belong to a number of Societies which have pretensions or at least desires to influence the value system of our culture. I even make contributions to political candidates if my convictions are strong enough, so that, as a citizen, I function as an individual who does attempt to influence the direction in which the culture goes. But, as a scientist, I'm afraid that I would find it very difficult to sign a pledge that I would not work in one or another area of pharmacogenetics or of psychomorphology even though some of the results might be potentially "explosive."

*I think it is necessary that some kind of control be provided for the scientific discoveries which we do make.* But this is something quite different than the scientist cutting off his curiosity in order to avert what may or may not turn out to be harmful. I suspect, in the long run, that if we are able to sustain the ban on the bomb as well as we have been able to do thus far, that all of those who signed up not to work on atomic power because it might lead to the destruction of mankind would have been proved completely wrong. The benefits of atomic power will far surpass anything that we have seen in the past in the form of energy. Even in our own field the introduction of radioisotopes provides an ability to follow and determine what is going on in some of the biochemistry and pharmacology. Had we taken the position that working on the bomb was evil and we wouldn't do it, it's possible that we would have cut ourselves off from something that may prove to be of great benefit. I take the stand that as scientists qua scientists, it is not only our privilege, but our responsibility to follow as far as we can our research leads. At the same time, being members of a culture, we do have a responsibility in determining the direction our culture will take.

The scientist probably knows much better than most others the direction in which a scientific discovery may lead. He often has been proved wrong, but I do think he has some responsibility to try to impart to society as best he sees them the implications of any particular discovery which happens to come his way.
*Mr. Koestler*: The problem which mention of the year 2000 poses is survival. The problem facing neuropsychopharmacology is to try to assure the survival of the species somehow. That's why I discussed the paranoic streak in man, and the possibilities, remote but not fantastic, of counteracting it.

Any legislation made to prevent tampering with human nature will be purely theoretical for a very simple reason—the investigation of viruses, bacteria and chemicals can always and with great justification be described as a defensive measure to counteract the possibility of virus attack or chemical attack. Also, as Nate Kline said, "you know, once Mount Everest is there, it will be climbed, nothing will prevent us from climbing it, because it's there."

I think the emphasis should be on tampering with the phenotype and not with the genotype. At present, tampering with the genotype still amounts to throwing a monkey wrench into a terribly complicated machine, except in the case of eliminating quite obvious deficiences. But if the danger to our species is as real and as urgent as in our more lucid moments we know it to be, but in our more relaxed moments tend to forget—if the danger is as urgent, then I think we ought to concentrate on the possibilities of counteracting this collective paranoia, this fatal preparedness not only to kill, but to die for a cause which might be good, bad or totally hairbrained.

*Mr. Campbell*: This is something that I have had a lot of fun with—try this as an interesting psychological point and you will find that children answer this correctly more often than adults. You've been out to the zoo and taken a look at all the animals that you see around there—of them all, which is the most deadly, dangerous, fighting creature? You don't ordinarily get the answer from adults but sometimes you do get the right answer from the children. Man—the one that puts all the others in cages. *Man as an animal* with no other equipment than his own physical self is the most deadly, dangerous, fighting creature that four billion years of evolution on this planet have been able to produce, and that is the reason and the only reason why he runs the planet. Practically every other living species on this planet gets out of the way of man. There are very few exceptions. The sharks do not yet recognize that man is dangerous. That's because we haven't been in the water enough. Give us a little time and they'll learn too. Man as an animal is a deadly, dangerous creature. I think that we will have to exemplify this before people can recognize it.

Item: A Union Pacific Track superintendent was out doing a

cruise along the track to see how things were going and what needed replacing and so on, plodding along the tracks up in the Rockies and a grizzly bear came out of the hills. Evidently it was in a foul mood; it went after him. He did not have a gun, he did not have a knife and he was no great woodsman. Five minutes later the bear was dead and the superintendent had not been scratched. He had been on the tracks there as I say, but one attribute he did have was that he was a semipro baseball pitcher. Within ten seconds the bear was blind in both eyes. He had a great fast ball and when you hitch that on to a piece of track ballast, it's deadly. All right, here's a man, and this is what a man can do.

Item: On one of Carl Akley's expeditions to Africa collecting for the Museum of Natural History a white African hunter was employed—he was a native African—for five generations his people had grown up in Africa. He knew the country. Akley asked him to go out in the bush to get some botanical specimens they wanted and he had gone out, not carrying his gun any more than you would carry yours if you went out into the local woods. Normally, there is nothing around that would want to bother man. Man is too dangerous and the animals know it. Lions prefer to leave man alone. The hunter encountered a pair of leopards. Ordinarily leopards are solitary hunters but this, apparently, was a newly mated pair, and the pair jumped him together. He came back to camp a little bit clawed up with two dead leopards. He had grabbed leopard number one and used it as a flail to kill leopard number two.

My point is this, that man as an animal is so much more dangerous than any other animal on earth. No other animal can possibly cull man. *But any living species must be culled.* It *has* to be culled somehow.

A few million years ago the ichthyosaurs reached the point of such dominance of the seas that nothing could cull them, nothing did cull them. That whole line of evolution died out due to arthritis and an accumulation of genetic defects because nothing culled the ichthyosaurs.

There's a reason for man's wars. War is the only way that the human species can be culled.

A group of businessmen out in Seattle bought an island off

the coast of Alaska. There was a herd of deer on it and some wolves. They got professional hunters to kill off the wolves so that there would be more deer for them to hunt. Five years later they hired professional hunters in Alaska to capture live wolves and take them to the island because the deer on the island were scrawny, diseased, weak and few in number. The deer had bred and eaten themselves into starvation. After the wolves were restored to the island, the deer became healthy again and the system went on fine.

Any living species must be culled and man is the only species on this planet capable of culling man. That's why we have war. *Dr. Kline*: It isn't necessarily brains either that lead to survival. There's a piece of poetry very much to the point about the brontosaurus:

> Behold the ancient Brontosaur,
> Famed in prehistoric lore,
> Not only for his width and length,
> But for his intellectual strength.
> You will observe by his remains,
> The creature had two sets of brains.
> One at his head, the usual place,
> The other at his spinal base.
> Thus he could reason a priori
> As well as a posteriori
> No problem bothered him a bit
> He made both head and tail of it
> If something slipped his forward mind
> 'Twas rescued by the one behind.
> And if in error he was caught
> He had a saving afterthought
> Behold this creature without peers
> Extinct at least six million years.

*Prof. Montagu*: Man finds himself at the present time in a condition in which he is threatened with imminent extinction, and this imminence is principally the doing of the scientist, whether he is aware of it or not. The scientist alone has created the means by which this has become a reality, no matter who put these means to practical use. Hitler never invented a new kind of biochemical means of exterminating his fellow men, but he could employ special kinds of men who were scientists and who were members of the highest academies to develop Cyclon B to murder 6½ million Jews. Liberty is not, as Lord Acton said, for anyone, and particularly, in my opinion, a scientist, the freedom to do what you like, but must be interpreted as meaning the right to be able to do what you ought. Scientists have become God-like creatures. This is the very meaning of the first Book of Genesis, namely the story of the expulsion of Adam and Eve from the Garden of Eden for having eaten of the tree of the Knowledge of Good and Evil. As Satan pointed out, God did not want man to do this because he feared that man would become as one of the Gods. Indeed, this is precisely what has happened to the scientist who uses his good knowledge as if it were in any use good, when in fact its effects can be lethal.

It is *not* man as an animal who creates disorder. The human being who learns according to the culture in which he has been conditioned becomes the deadly creature. I do not think that there exists a paranoid-schizophrenic streak in man which can, in any way, be held to be innate or that has any genetic substrates whatever that are the product of evolution. I think that all these behaviors are learned ones, and we can unlearn them and replace them with sounds of forms of behavior.

*Mr. Koestler*: But one question, Ashley. Don't you think that if we learned from the beginning of history always to do the wrong headed things, there must BE a propensity or predisposition, a genetic predisposition to learn the wrong things.

*Prof. Montagu*: Yes, there is a genetic predisposition to learn anything—wrong things as well as right things, not because they are right and not because they are wrong, but simply because they are learnable.

*Dr. Kline*: Speaking of setting up restrictions and laws, Lord Acton also pointed out, "If a law is not absolutely necessary, then it is absolutely necessary that there not be a law." This is the scientist's point of view; he feels that he should keep his options open knowing that those things which look as if they may be helpful often turn out to be otherwise, and those that appear frightening may turn out to be very helpful.

*Judge Oliver*: Man has been struggling for a long, long time to settle controversy without resort to violence. The more civilized the country, the less punitive is the criminal sanction. When an official taboo is enacted into law, society puts the violator in jail so that he can no longer move freely within organized society. There is, however, great difficulty in trying to classify what is moral, what is immoral, what is good, what is bad. The prime problem is one of methods under which a particular government may lawfully decide what is good, bad or indifferent.

Open violations of the Harrison Narcotic Act have been advocated. Violations of the first and fourth paragraph of the Comstock Act were recommended. Anthony Comstock is a very, very good example of a man who was convinced that he could identify that which is obscene. Experience, however, has shown that what is obscene is in the eye of the beholder. We get in very, very difficult terrain unless we recognize that a democratic system is predicated on the idea that, subject to appropriate constitutional limitations, we count noses to elect people to make judgments, for good or bad, as to what will be permitted and what will not be permitted in the community. The great opportunity, as I see it, for man to get out of his perilous condition is to develop the techniques of public education upon which, in the final analysis, he must rely. We must come to understand how we can transmit to the general public the knowledge of many, many diversified disciplines which have become more and more withdrawn from the general community than any prior time in our history.

*Mr. Koestler:* Lord Acton and the responsibility of the scientist and the irresponsibility of the scientist and the dangers of science aside, it is important to discuss the possible positive contributions of science in general, and neuropsychopharmacology in particular to the aim of surviving to the year 2000. Assuming we discover the ideal anti-suggestibility drug—not a tranquilizer, but a mental harmonizer—how can we persuade seven hundred million Chinese to take it? Or the simpler question is how do we persuade Indian women to take the birth-control pill? These are the technical questions. These are the questions worth discussing.

*Dr. Kline:* In *Opus 21* Phillip Wylie describes some future society in which there is a drug which will cure any existing disease and prevent the acquisition of others. It is an absolutely perfect prophylactic and it is also effective no matter how severe the illness—whether cancer or any other serious disease. It also cures all diseases. It has only one side effect, and that is that the person using it turns green. No one will take the drug because as soon as someone appears green it is obvious that had they not taken the drug they would have been dreadfully diseased or dead. It is a terrible problem to get people to take what is "good" for them, whatever that means. Now it may be that tranquilization may just be another path to the extinction of the species. It may be that a certain amount of disruption, disharmony, instability is part of what gives us the thrust to keep moving, so I'm not sure that tranquility is really what one should aim for.

*Mr. Koestler*: Man is, as Waddington called it, a belief-accepting animal. He accepts beliefs very easily. He's suggestible. Long before the mass media came into existence, man was suggestible. The prophet Mohammed got a human avalanche going without radio and without television. Now we have drugs which increase suggestibility. Can we have drugs, are they within reach, which counteract suggestibility and the acceptance of beliefs and fanaticism, sacrifice and self-sacrifice?

The individual G.I. is prepared not only to kill but also to die out of loyalty to his Government. The egotism of the group feeds on the altruism of the individual, his altruism and his suggestibility, so we must counteract suggestibility. But assuming we discover the means to counteract it, how do we persuade people and governments to let the means spread? I don't know the answer, but I know that certain drugs which have pleasant effects spread over the world without any government sponsorship, for instance, alcohol, barbiturates, tranquilizers.

*Dr. Kline*: There has always been rather unsuccessful resistance to tobacco. The first person who smoked in Europe was a seaman who had sailed on Columbus's expedition. When he landed in Spain, he had cigars, which were what the American Indians smoked, and being a good tourist he wanted to show the folks back home what was being done. Having smoked a cigar he was promptly clamped into jail by the Inquisition on the grounds that anyone who could exhale smoke from his lungs must be in league with the devil. He literally spent three years in confinement. The history of the spread of smoking in Europe is a curious and interesting one. It was used as a medical treatment for many years and then it became a favorite source of tax revenue, which it still is, incidentally. One of the reasons why James I of England, who was very much against it, finally was convinced to permit it was that he needed money for the Treasury.

Now, it may well be that we could make drugs which serve some useful purpose attractive enough to become addictive. Perhaps we should build into the appropriate drugs some addicting factors so that we would be inclined to use them rather than avoid them.

*Judge Oliver*: I would like to mention three things—vaccination (approximately 18th Century), fluoridation of water, birth control. There was reasonable unanimity that it was a good thing to prevent smallpox. But that took a long time in coming. Today, to start a grade A political row in any community in the United States, put fluoridation of water on a referendum. All kinds of people will talk about playing the part of the Devil and tampering with human nature and upsetting the cycle of nature and violating God's Law and all that business.

As for birth control—we see one of the most ancient organized institutions going through the process of ground shifting at the present time. But it will take time.

In order for a drug to have appropriate regulation, appropriate in the sense that a competent group of scientists, whoever they may be, would advocate the use of the particular drug, the public must acquire as a part of their learning, a sufficient agreement that one is not in fact playing the part of the Devil, that he is not violating somebody's religion, that he's not doing a great many things that always put a drag upon any change within any legal framework.

*Dr. Elkes* (from the audience): I find an unholy alliance between Mr. Koestler and Mr. Campbell. Mr. Campbell gave us a taste of what is ahead for us in evolution. He implied that evolution did not care much whether we liked what was coming or not—and predicted (not without a certain delight) that we would like our future less and less. He may be right. Perhaps the future intends to carry us beyond good and evil. Perhaps the good man of tomorrow will be the cold man of today.

But I am more worried about Mr. Koestler's "present" than Mr. Campbell's "future." For, says Mr. Koestler—and here I find the alliance strange, and distressing—we are victims of an excess of love, displaced love, and we are in danger of blowing up. Does he mean love, or does he mean feeling, or does he perhaps mean an old attribute, territoriality, invested with feeling? Is not impersonal love firmly rooted in hate, and is not "the love that passeth understanding" the evolutionary twin of a hate which man finds even harder to understand—until he deliberately sets about to do so, as he is doing now. After all, we have survived, man's blundering notwithstanding, using devices which we have evolved as our defenses against these pack-hunting propensities. We have invented the institution of Work, the device of Play, the huge structure of Religion, the vast symbolic world of Art. Our cultures are vast defensive and substitutive systems. Though the attitudes of 'Taking' and 'Control' have so far won it over 'Giving' and 'Letting Go," times, I think, are changing, at least for individuals. If Mr. Koestler means that we are excessively invested in our things and symbols, and use them to satisfy old territorial needs—if this is the 'love' he means (the counterpart of which is the paranoia of threatened loss)—I am with him. But of People-to-people love we have too little, not too much. For the thing/love and symbol/love make people/love harder to come by, especially self-love and self-regard and self-esteem. Things balance out. True self-ness and self-regard is the condition of true selflessness. Is a reach-for-the-pill solution a serious way of saving our collective necks? Should we add soma to our drinking water? Or could it be that the drug culture and the drug utopia are merely rash and fever, signifying a much deeper disorder in our society. In an over-populated thing-world people are getting steadily more passive and more lonely, or more violent and herd-ridden. Talk and Being-With in small groups is rare; it has to be deliberately cultivated in order to survive at all. Until we know more about the natural chemistry of coping and communication, pills will make for more, rather than less, loneliness, even if they can abate violence. They will not replace communication, the sharing of feeling—positive feeling—between a few people (which is all we can handle, anyway). Of that kind of sentiment there is too little, not too much. It is this kind of reward—love is the word—which man seems to be obstinately pursuing.

*Mr. Koestler*: I am accused of wanting to sprinkle drugs on the Chinese. No, I emphatically underlined that the problem is to make the cure spread voluntarily—not to "sprinkle" but to persuade. You impute to me a crudely materialistic view and a crudely pessimistic view of man, which has no place for creativity, art and so on. Well, may I mention as a mitigating circumstance that before this last book I wrote *The Act of Creation,* which discussed creativity and art for 760 pages—which is twice the length of *The Ghost in the Machine.* But the fact that Van Gogh painted wonderful pictures does not contradict the fact that he cut off his ear and was a raving schizophrenic. The creativity of man and the tragic madness of man are two sides of the same medal. Then again you emphasized the glories of man's symbolic activities, his unique possession of language as a vehicle of communication and of social inheritance. But I have tried to point out that language has also this terrifying destructive aspect of erecting barriers, creating slogans and crystallizing ideologies. You really have to look at both sides of the medal. Let me repeat that man's knowledge of death made pyramids rise out of the desert sand, but it also populated the atmosphere with demonic presences, like those in a mental home, which persecute the inmates. I don't want to end on a note of despair. I hope that science can do something, more particularly psychopharmacology. Perhaps this is a very naïve hope, but it is better than no hope at all. I am impatient with what I call the "if only" ideology: *If only* people would listen to reason, everything would be all right; *If only* we could devise a perfect educational system, it would solve all problems. This pious sermonizing has been tried from the days of the Hebrew prophets and the Christian martyrs, and on to the American pragmatists and the German metaphysicians—it has been tried and tried, and yet man's history is the mess which it is.

*Prof. Montagu*: Educational systems in earlier times never succeeded because they were never based on the findings of science. For the first time in the history of 2½ million years of man's evolution we do now have scientifically verifiable facts as to what man requires in order to develop as a healthy, cooperative, loving human being.

*Prof. Zubin* (from the audience): Recently we have been trying to find out whether there is a survival value to schizophrenia since a mutation rate is too low to explain the incidence of this disorder. In an article which was published recently in the *Journal of General Psychology,* Dr. Hammer and I concluded that unpredictability of behavior is the essential heritable trait underlying schizophrenia. It can go in one direction leading to schizophrenia if society looks with disfavor on the behavior, and in the other direction leading to creativity if society values the behavior. When all the chips are down, this seems to be the essential element in schizophrenia. We all believe that the law regards science as self-correcting, so that if we are wrong this year, next year we will find what is wrong and the law can accept our corrected version, but if the law gets in the middle before science has been able to straighten itself out, it always causes terrific trouble. For example, there is the case of PKU, where the law stepped in before science knew all the answers. As a result laws have been enacted in thirty-two states regarding phenylalanine-free diets which prevent the possibility of even having control groups. In these states the law requires that tests for phenylalanine be given to neonates and the moment that the test indicates that the titre is above a certain amount, the restricted diet must be applied. Can we ask the law and the judges to stop making laws before science has reached a point where the findings are tenable? Can't we afford to be five years behind times with regard to the law? Otherwise, one of the safeguards the law has established—the self-correcting nature of science, will be nullified.

*Judge Oliver*: Well, that question is easy for a judge to answer. Your complaint should be directed to the Congress. Judges do not make laws. Judges apply law.

The interesting thing is that there is a great kinship between judges and the scientific community—always has been. The great flexibility of the common law is such that there is no real law and science in making adjustments in regard to concepts of criminal responsibility in light of added scientific knowledge of mental illness. Most young psychiatrists when they first come to Springfield Medical Center do not, however, understand this. They have been subjected to a couple of lectures in medical school and honestly believe that McNaughton is still the law. Indeed they have all kinds of concepts of what they believe they are going to be required to work with the next two years of their lives. My court established a panel of psychiatrists in 1963, the first in the United States. That experiment has spread without any Congressional assistance to over half the judicial districts in the country. It is to the great credit of medicine that this concept of law and science cooperation will work.

Congress would hesitate to act if science is able to articulate why no law should be passed. But if there is total silence from the responsible scientific community then Congress acts in response to what they hear from very noisy people. After all, a congressman does run every two years and if he talks to you and gets accurate information, he is going to say, "you must explain this to my people back home" because, back home, they are flooded with all kinds of talk as to how bad things are. The problem really is not the application of a law. The real difficulty is the enactment of the law. If the Congress can be said to go off half-cocked, we must understand that the reason it goes off half-cocked is that it has acted on the only information given it.

*Dr. Kline*: Let me point out that to some extent there is a similar conflict even within our own group, between the practicing physician who has to treat and the scientist who says "we are not ready yet to treat." One is obliged to use the best knowledge available even though it subsequently turns out to have been wrong.

*Prof. Montagu*: Well, we've been considering here one tree in a very large forest, namely, the tree on which drugs grow, and we have been talking about it as if it were the sole means by which we are going to save humanity, when I am sure most of us have no such idea in mind, and I think it is important for us to remember that this will be only one means—if it proves to be a means at all—by which we may change man in some direction. We can, at least, in a sufficient number agree upon what is a desirable one. I do think it is necessary, however, for us to remember that there are a large number of these other trees all of which will also require attention. Principally, it is not so much the trees that will require our attention, but the soil in which they grow. It is that soil that I mean when I use the word "education" in its Latin meaning, not as it is mis-etymologized by the educators, as "educere" which they also mispronounce, meaning to draw out, but as "educare"—to care for, to nourish, and to cause to grow. This is the education of which we have so little, and in which I put all my faith for the future. We must minister to the needs of this newborn creature to grow and develop as a warm, loving human being who will live as if to live and love were one. This is what I believe we must concentrate our attention on, principally the control of that one phenomenon in the universe which we describe as a 150-pound nonlinear servo-mechanism which can be wholly reproduced by unskilled labor!

*Mr. Koestler:* Very often people seem to quarrel about principles, when the argument is in reality not about principles but about priorities and emphasis. It is obvious that education is a kingpin in human history. Education is a good thing, but it is not enough. It hasn't been enough for the last seven thousand years, and it isn't enough today to prevent the explosion. The word "explosion" was missing from our discussion. Listening to this panel one might have thought we are living in Lotusland. The sense of urgency was completely absent from our list of priorities. However naïve it may sound, on my own list the top priority is medicine in the widest sense. Listening to your nice, naïve sermons that hope is perhaps not so naïve after all. I would like to end on that note.

## Epilogue

*Dr. Evans:* Shall we heed Mr. Koestler's advice or will we wait too long? So few people understand the proper use of drugs and so many uninformed prejudices exist, I can only hope. Can we medicate ourselves wisely? We are on the edge of a "choose your mood" society. Chemicals which affect the mind, as pollutants, prescribed or "over-the-counter" drugs, foods and beverages and even "incapacitating" chemical warfare agents are every where, used by every one, every day. Yet, the simplest principles of pharmacology are not taught in our schools. *We must teach the public the proper way to use these chemicals (drugs) so that as little harm results as is possible. Drugs are not "abused," but uninformed people are abused by misusing drugs. No drug is harmful if properly used. No drug is safe if used without knowledge and caution.* So far, we have failed in our task of teaching the correct use of drugs. We have been too distracted by the "Drug Problem" to study the "Health Problem." If this situation continues, the world in the year 2000 may be a nightmare.

### EDITOR'S NOTES

1. Since the meeting of the panel, the American College of Neuropsychopharmacology has expanded the duties of its Ethics Committee to examine any ethically improper uses of mind-altering drugs in society as a whole and created a new committee for "Issue of Public Concern."

2. Tobacco use, improper use of "over-the-counter" drugs and, on the other side, the relative failure to obtain adequate fluoridation of water supplies further substantiates our almost total failure in the control of the patterns of chemical uses in this country.

3. Since the meeting, *The Interim Report of the Commission of Inquiry into the Non-Medical Use of Drugs,* Queen's Printer, Ottawa, has been presented to the Canadian Parliament; and the U. S. National Institute of Mental Health has submitted its first of a series of studies on this subject as a report to the U. S. Congress, *Marihuana and Health,* 1971, Government Printing Office, Washington.

# NAME INDEX

# SUBJECT INDEX